THE STORIES OF A
WEST VIRGINIA DOCTOR

Harold D. Almond, M.D.

International Standard Book Number 0-87012-583-4
Library of Congress Control Number 97-093910
Printed in the United States of America
Copyright © 1997 by Harold D. Almond, M.D.
Buckhannon, WV
All Rights Reserved
1997

Third Printing 2003

Camera-ready material provided.

McClain Printing Company
Parsons, West Virginia 26287
www.mcclainprinting.com
2003

DEDICATION

Dedicated to the loving memory of my best friend, my wife, Lois. And to our children--Greenbrier, K, Anne, Ruthie, and Beth--who added joy and pride to our lives. And to all my collies, who faithfully loved their master as he loved them.

ACKNOWLEDGMENTS

A special thanks to my children for their enthusiasm and help. To my doctor son, Greenbrier, for always asking questions and carefully listening to my stories. To my oldest daughter, K, for her frequent visits to look after daily details and for our hours of good talks. To my daughter, Anne, for her organizational talent as she undertook the task of editor for my book. To my daughter, Ruthie, for her numerous letters and calls of support. To my daughter, Beth, for her writing contributions and her eagle-eye proofreading. To my son-in-law, Richard, for using his computer expertise to format my book. I also wish to thank my friend, Judy Knorr, for her word-processing and proofreading assistance. I especially wish to thank my medical colleagues, my nursing staff, and my patients, who blessed me with a long and satisfying practice.

CONTENTS

PREFACE

I practiced medicine in central West Virginia for forty years. I had a small jeep that covered our area and over into the surrounding counties. The first four months were not busy and my wife Lois and I and our two children used up some of the savings we had from the two years spent in the Army Air Force in Nebraska and in Japan. But then in the winter of 1950, we had the "finest" flu epidemic Upshur County ever had. I suddenly had as many patients as I could handle and ran the jeep over rock base and mud roads. After that winter, I was always busy.

When I first started my practice in Buckhannon, I worked with a small, close-knit group of physicians—Dr. Basil Page, Dr. Jake Huffman, and Dr. Bob Chamberlain. We were all busy and we liked each other and we helped each other out in our rural county. We had a small, but good, hospital which was run by the Catholic Sisters.

During my forty years, I delivered about 3200 babies, about half the number of Dr. Huffman, and about the same number as Dr. Chamberlain. I assisted Dr. Page in surgery on his patients, Dr. Huffman's patients, and my own. Dr. Page, the most senior of our group, was a good diagnostician, a fine surgeon, and he did excellent orthopedic surgery.

Somewhere late in my practice I met Jim Comstock, Editor of the <u>West Virginia Hillbilly</u> newspaper. Once when he spoke to our West Virginia Medical Meeting, he said that doctors had at least one case every day that was so interesting that it could be reported. He got me thinking that he was right, and I wrote some thirty cases for the <u>Hillbilly</u>. No one ever wrote a letter to the editor saying that they liked the stories, but Jim Comstock kept begging West Virginia doctors to follow in Dr. Harold Almond's footsteps.

I retired at age 75 and wrote other stories for my grandchildren. Why not a book of stories about my forty

1

years as a West Virginia doctor? I've written stories about all aspects of my practice, as well as a piece about Dr. James Cunningham, the oldest doctor in West Virginia. He lived and practiced at Pickens for sixty-five years. In fact, I have lectured about him being the only doctor in West Virginia who has taken care of a leper. I have talked to 300 to 450 visitors each year at the newly built Doctor Museum in Pickens for the last ten years at the annual Maple Syrup Festival. It has occurred the third week end in March for the last fifteen years or so.

If this contribution to the reader is successful, I am going to get other groups of doctors in clinics and hospitals throughout our state to record their findings in a book that they write. Then we will select the best of these stories in one book, The Best Doctor Stories of West Virginia. These will challenge other states like Nebraska and New York to do likewise. Ultimately, I hope that the American Medical Association will select the best stories of all fifty states and put them into one book.

Jim Comstock would be pleased with my enthusiasm. Time will tell.

Dr. Harold D. Almond
Buckhannon, West Virginia
June 1, 1997

HOUSE CALLS

A COLD NIGHT TO REMEMBER

In late 1949, I settled down in wild, rural West Virginia with my family to open my practice as a General Practitioner. Medical School, Internship, and service in the Army Air Force were completed.

When I first started my practice, taking care of patients in their own homes was routine. I always liked to make house calls, even if I had to travel a far distance in my little jeep. I liked the solitude and the scenery. Many rural folks without reliable transportation in the 1950's and 1960's needed and were thankful for a doctor who would come see them when they were sick. But sometimes, traveling country roads could be difficult and even dangerous.

Late one night I made a house call down the Hall Road. I crossed under the railroad track, passed the church, and drove my jeep down to the rock quarry where the State Road had taken out tons of rock for the county road. It was wet, half rain and half snow. The Buckhannon River was high, but not out of its bank. There were chunks of ice floating down stream.

The road ended suddenly at the edge of the river. The brother of my sick patient was waiting with a row boat. The brother seemed a bit strange, but I knew he had been receiving treatment for a mental sickness by a psychiatrist in Baltimore. "Do you want to row, or should I?" he asked. I elected to row, and he climbed in the front end of the row boat. Half way across the river, he sneaked up and squeezed my thyroid bone and neck. I was mad and full of pain. I tossed that one-hundred and nine pound man into the river and he gasped for breath. Lucky for him, I had tossed him up stream. He swam to the boat, and I pulled him up. We floated down seventy-five yards or more and I lost an oar. I paddled to the far shore with one oar, and the two of us ran up to his cottage. He was soaking wet, and I was just wet.

When we reached the house, I examined his sister, gave her a shot, and left medicine. I dried out, paddled back across the river, and tied up the boat and hiked back upstream. I was cold, damp, and shivering. I turned up the heater in my jeep and hurried home. I took a long, hot shower and climbed into bed, still cold.

Fifteen minutes later a call came from Pickens to see a patient up on Turkey Bone Mountain. I told the caller I could come but I couldn't walk because I was still half frozen. "You will not have to walk a step," she assured me over the phone.

I drove through deep snow and reached the Pickens road in about ninety minutes. Tony, the patient's son, met me at the crossroads and told me we had to walk three miles upward to see his mother because the snow had closed the road. He grabbed my doctor bag, and I followed his footsteps. It was blowing and cold by this time. Tony's mother was very sick. I gave her a shot, aspirin and codeine, and then climbed into a bed of bear skins and slept well until daylight. After breakfast, a man arrived with a horse and sled. We headed for Pickens and soon came to the Pickens road. Even though we had made good time back, the short trip made me cold again. My jeep wouldn't start, so the horse pulled me downhill until the motor turned over. I was on my way home with the heater going full blast. No, I didn't catch pneumonia, not even a cold. It was a night to remember.

PAYING THE BILL

Through my years of practice, I cared for many rural patients who had very little money. Many times, my patients would "pay" my bills by delivering a load of firewood, a bushel of tomatoes or cucumbers, a side of venison (which was usually dressed, much to the relief of Lois), or even a squirrel or rabbit. Sometimes, however, patients were never able to pay for my services. I learned to accept what came and tried to care for all of my patients equally with compassion and the best possible medical treatment available.

An elderly gentleman whom I had taken care of for a number of years, developed a malignancy, probably of the pancreas. He lived twenty-five miles "up the country." He had limited resources and limited mobility. His family was caring for him at home. In the course of his terminal care, I made two or three trips to the house and as financial resources were limited, I made a minimal charge. I had an interesting visit with the family and returned home. Each time the family seemed to appreciate the care that I gave, even though there was little I could do other than monitor his progress and try to manage his discomforts.

Approximately six months after he died, his wife came in for the only appointment she ever kept after his death. After her exam, evaluation and discussion, she said, "Doc, I have paid off the undertaker; now I am ready to start paying on your bill." It was a good thing I didn't count on her promise. That was the last I ever heard from her.

A HOUSE CALL MADE BY A SICK DOCTOR

Late in the summer of 1951, I treated a patient who had typhoid. I took my typhoid booster shot and immediately got a reaction. My hands and feet swelled and I hurt in most of my joints, but especially in my buttocks whenever I hit a hole in the county roads. I was in real misery.

I planned to take a night off and recover, but then a call came from Wildcat.

A Lewis County doctor had delivered a baby three days previously and the mother wasn't doing well. I couldn't find what the problem was, but the son was begging for help. I told him I couldn't walk more than fifty feet. He said I wouldn't have to walk at all.

Off to Wildcat, I used one swollen hand at a time to steer. I drove slower than usual because my sitter was aggravated with each bump, especially the road past Ireland and Babylon. The night was beautiful, almost a full moon.

I met the patient's son at the bridge crossing the Little Kanawha River, and he hopped in my jeep. We drove down a field for a couple of hundred yards. The road dead-ended at the river. That was the end of my ride. We rowed across the river; then we started walking up a poorly defined path straight up the mountain. The lad took my doctor bags and pulled me up and up. I hurt all over. He said there were no wildcats around, but I jumped almost out of my skin when a hoot owl screamed out in dark shadows. My shoes wouldn't fit and my swollen feet hurt. I hurt in my ribs when I breathed. All my hiking days on the Appalachian Trail were easier than that quarter of a mile uphill walk that night. The dog we met at the house barked and growled, but wagged his tail and was friendly when the lad whistled back to him.

The baby was a girl and was healthy, but the mother had already expired by the time I finally arrived, apparently from a post partum hemorrhage.

Now I felt really sick. The trip alone down that hill and across the river by boat was too much. I sat and panted in my little jeep until finally I got my breath and recovered from the hurting.

A Nursing Student's Story

Shirley, the daughter of my wife's cousin, was a Sophomore in the first nursing class at West Virginia University back in 1963. She had come to our house for spring break instead of traveling home. She brought her pharmacy books to study action and doses of drugs.

Shirley was restless; she had studied hard that second year of nursing, and she needed some practical training. She made hospital rounds with me and she saw her first delivery. Dr. Page, our surgeon, whose daughter was a nurse, invited her to scrub the next day and help deliver a Cesarean section. So, on the morrow she stood alongside our Registered Nurses, scrubbed and gowned up. As a nurse, she cut long ends of the knot and suture; she passed a hemostat; and was the first to hold the newborn.

She was too excited to study that afternoon, so she helped me in the office. She gave her first immunization to a one-year-old child, gave a gold shot to an elderly citizen in the gluteus maximus muscle, and drew blood for a lab test. She was good.

When she got to our home that evening, she was on cloud nine. She told Lois and our children all the exciting things she had done that day. We reviewed her lists of medications, some given in grains and some given in milligrams, some in capsule form, other in tablets, and in teaspoon doses.

Sunday was a day off, but after church, Shirley and I drove out to the country over a rock base road and then up a farm road. It was raining and cool and we talked to the farmer's wife about her invalid Mother. She was sitting at the fire, cracking hickory nuts on the 4" core of rock about ten inches long. Shirley never had seen anyone crack hickory nuts perfectly with one blow of a hammer. It must have been the core of rock. Where did the core come from? Shirley wondered. The farmer's wife told her the core came from this very farm. They had drilled for gold here years ago, and there were fifty or more holes and lots of cores left over. Shirley was skeptical, but then I told her that eight miles away the Indians had dug for gold at Ash Camp. I, too, had dug at Ash Camp. I never found gold, but there beneath the ledge of rock is a very well-dug 50' by 60' piece of real estate. We were curious and we each took a core back home with us after visiting with our patient. Years later, I had a chemist friend run an analysis and there was almost one cent worth of gold.

The next afternoon, Shirley, Lois, and I were called to a farm house about ten miles from town. The six-week-old baby was sick. Unique in my practice was this family of children, a husband, and two wives. I had made calls there previously, and Lois or I always had to ask which woman was the Mother. Yes, I had delivered children from both wives. The first wife was the nurse for all, and she always did a fine job. The baby was the latest from wife number two. I told Shirley I would give her a dollar after we had visited if she would tell me who the Mother was. She didn't believe the story of a family with one husband and two wives. Shirley and I examined the baby, and it was sick with pharyngitis and bronchitis, i.e., infection of the respiratory tract. I gave the penicillin shot, and Shirley prepared the penicillin to be taken by mouth and wrote the instructions on the bottle. The mother who helped us agreed to call us tomorrow as to the baby's condition. On route home, Shirley was silent and thinking, "Patients in practice are different from patients in West Virginia University Hospital." Shirley didn't get the dollar.

Shirley studied a few days. We drove up to Pickens on Valentine's Day to see a sick baby. Pickens is the snow capital of West Virginia and that February day it was snowing on top of two and one half feet on the ground. After seeing the baby, we hiked up to the home of the oldest doctor in the state—Dr. Cunningham. Shirley pinned a red rose on his lapel and I used my Polaroid several times and got a few good pictures. Shirley was excited; she had met the only doctor in West Virginia who ever cared for a leper. He was 100 years old now. Coming home, the little Jeep skidded some and we backed out of a drift. I reminded Shirley that Dr. Cunningham had outlived fourteen horses, and we were lucky. We were warm and dry.

I mailed a picture with Shirley pinning the rose on Dr. Cunningham's lapel to the local media, and I told her

11

undoubtedly that she would be on television news at 6:00 p.m. the next night. Shirley went back to the University the very next day. She told her nursing friends her adventures giving gold shots, helping with a Cesarean section, watching a normal delivery, visiting a family with one husband and two wives, and visiting the oldest doctor in West Virginia. She told me later that there were a lot of doubters, but when the six p.m. news came on, she told them she wanted to see her picture on television. Sure enough, the first picture on the news was that of the famous leper doctor receiving a red rose. A day later, a picture appeared in the press, and a month later, a picture and a short article appeared in the West Virginia Medical Journal.

Shirley is married now, teaching nursing, and has a daughter of her own, and lives in the MidWest. Somewhere is the Polaroid picture of that student nurse. We had better find it for her daughter so she will know that all of this really happened to her mother.

IDENTIFY YOURSELF

One night at about 2:00 a.m. I got a call from a woman who lived on College Avenue. The patient said she had a respiratory infection. I told her I would be right there, and I was at her house within ten minutes. I knocked. She asked who it was. A dumb question, I thought, so I kiddingly said I was a burglar. A dumb answer. She opened the door with a revolver in her hand! I immediately identified myself as her doctor, and I showed her the doctor's bag. Once she believed me, she invited me in and I checked her out and supplied her with the needed medicine. She then showed me the corner of her living room where she had put three bullets through the floor when someone tried to break into her house. The next day, I talked to the local police about her and they said they had been to her home several times when called about previous burglars. That night, I could hardly sleep a wink.

TRAVELING THE MUDDY ROADS

A call came one Tuesday night from the Brethren Church located on the Middle Fork River at Woodley Abutment, a small town near the old lumber town of Ellamore. Woodley Abutment got its name because it is the location of a wooden bridge that spans the Middle Fork River from Barbour County as the old Staunton-Parkersburg Pike crosses through mid West Virginia.

The man said his preacher was lying on the floor of his church and would I come and see him. It was after dark. It was cold and damp, with half snow and half rain falling. I had been down to Woodley Abutment with a patient/friend from her home a year or so before. We had gone down there from Mt. Nebo Church road, down past the old blacksmith shop. I remembered a steep, rocky road that was almost like a trail.

This time it was a mud road via Swamp Run Road. In fact, I got stuck in the mud with all four wheels a turning. I couldn't go forward or backward. I left the engine slowly running in gear and stepped over my rubbers in mud and water. I started to push. Finally, the wheels took hold, and I jumped in and the jeep was out of the mud hole in a jiffy. I have used rock, and even hay, to put under the wheels on other occasions, but I found neither here that dark, rainy, snowy night.

Yes, the preacher had a stroke and needed to be hospitalized. I called the ambulance. Even though the ambulance had chains, it too got stuck in the same puddles, but finally somehow got moving again.

All our muddy travels were to no avail. Several days later the Brethren minister died at St. Joseph's Hospital. The road today is rock based and that mud hole has been drained well.

THE PILE OF COAL

Ice storms in West Virginia, at times, bring a lot of work for country doctors. A coal truck with tons of the best soft coal in all West Virginia, the Peerless Coal, slid off the county road that morning and upset in Mr. Vanderhoff's yard, near his home. The driver was treated for minor injuries and returned to help the wrecker retrieve his truck.

The coal remained in the yard. It didn't detract from the yard's appearance but bothered the old man. The owner dropped in several times that summer to say he would be back to get his coal, but he never came.

A year later, Mr. Vanderhoff had developed an acute anxiety reaction over the coal pile and against the owner. His blood pressure and pulse were up that hot June day, sixteen months later when I drove twenty-four miles to see him.

We cured his problem as soon as I informed him that he owned the mineral and coal rights if he covered the pile with plastic and three inches of dirt, some fertilizer, and clover seed.

The coal owner was hot under the collar when he assumed that the dirt and grass was mixed with his coal and thus rendered it useless for sale.

Mr. and Mrs. Vanderhoff opened up a small mine that coming winter. He warmed his house and lowered his blood pressure. He appreciated his doctor's prescription.

THE DOCTOR

(I like this poem by Dr. E. Leon Linger because we doctors who practiced medicine in the 1950's and 1960's often experienced nights just like this.)

The Doctor

The early morning sunlight was filtering through the
    trees
As up the walk he hurried, reaching for his keys.
And from a distant hillside the crowing of a cock
Carried to him faintly as he fumbled with the lock.
He entered through the doorway and closed it fast behind
As visions of his waiting bed kept running through his
    mind.
Then quickly off with shoes and socks, and ready for his
    bed
He stretched with happy sighing, and dropped his weary
    head.
But just as sleep descended, the jangling of the phone
Brought him sitting upright with strident, rasping tone.
And on the line, a worried voice, "Please come out right
    away!
The baby's sick and fevered, and will not eat or play."
So once again he had to dress, and with the morning sun,
Just as one day had ended, another had begun.
And thus it goes, day in, day out, for many of our friends
Who earned the title "Doctor", and all that word portends.

UNUSUAL DELIVERIES

A COLD NIGHT FOR A DELIVERY

When Lois and I came to Buckhannon in 1949, I was fortunate that there was an opening for a young GP like me. Another older doctor had retired recently from deliveries. I liked obstetrics. Part of my obstetrical training had been in the Chicago Clinic Maternity Center delivering babies in the home, so I thought I would try home deliveries. In 1950 in Upshur County, about fifty per cent were in the home and fifty per cent in the two local hospitals.

Our area in Upshur, Barbour, Randolph, and Lewis counties near Buckhannon in 1949-50 was poor; our roads and transportation were not good. Many mothers were unknown to me and had no prenatal care.

The temperature this night at the mill on Sand Run was close to zero and my arctics crunched on the snow as I left my jeep and carried my two bags—one obstetrical and the other my usual all-purpose house call bag—up to the miner's home in rural Upshur County.

The mother had received no prenatal care, but she had seven or eight other babies. I expected no difficulties, but the house was heated only with two fireplaces. There was space between the floor boards, and the wind and cold and some snow blew up through the crevices. The rocking chair was rocked only at right angles to the crevices. It was cold. I couldn't take my gloves off for any length of time. I refused the coffee, as it is a diuretic for me in the cold, and the outhouse was some sixty feet away.

I was happy for the mother and for me, too, that it was an extraordinarily easy delivery. In two and one-half hours, I started back home.

A GOAT EATS MY ROOF

In the summer of 1950, I was asked by one of the older physicians to attend to his maternity patient at Rangoon. He told me the home was clean, and the family was "good folks".

I arrived about midnight; the patient was having good contractions. I lay down to wait and fell asleep. When I awoke, I was startled to see it was daylight. The mother had slowed down her contractions, so I went out on the front porch. There on the cloth roof of my little jeep was the family goat eating the roof. The hole was directly over the driver's seat. I was mad, and my aim with a small rock was good. The goat came down in a hurry.

The patient stopped labor, so I returned to the office for a full day of work. About 1:00 p.m. a telephone call came telling me the baby had arrived. I returned to check the mother and baby. There was very little professional skill needed and I did not feel much satisfaction since I had not delivered the baby. At the end of the day, I fixed my goat-eaten roof with adhesive tape.

A LEAKY HOUSE

It was the evening of March 27, 1950. Money was tight, and I needed the $25.00 delivery fee to pay some outstanding bills. The patient had six children and I was told she had good contractions. The home was ten miles upstream from Buckhannon. It started to rain when I left the rock base road, and the last half mile was red and slippery with clay. This necessitated a shift to 4-wheel drive in my little jeep.

The house was small and over-crowded and the roof leaked badly. I draped my old military raincoat over the mother's bed and went back to my jeep to rest. It got cold without my raincoat that damp night. Four or five times, I started up the jeep and turned the heater on. The baby came about dawn, and about that time the sun came out. I left my raincoat with the mother; she needed it more than I.

STUCK IN THE SNOW

Late in November, 1950, Upshur County got fifty inches of snow in two days. The call requesting help with a home delivery that evening was to Hall, ten miles downstream. I called my school teacher friend Charlie to accompany me on that snowy night. The road was not plowed, so I drove my jeep down to Hodgesville, Century, Volga and Boulder and back up to Hall. It was bitter cold, only 10°, and the wind was still blowing.

The tenant farmer had used his team and a homemade wooden plow to clear the last half mile to the farm. I was in a hurry on this last half mile and the jeep slipped off over a small bank. The jeep wouldn't go forward or backward. Neither Charlie nor I took time to use the shovel. We ran down the lane and entered the old farm house just when the last of the kerosene was used up. The fireplace provided the entire light and heat. I asked for a kettle to boil the needle and syringe, but the single pot was too greasy to use. The mother took a morphine tablet by mouth and the baby came within the hour.

We kept hearing hooves stamping in the next room, so when the delivery was over, I asked the farmer if he would pull my jeep out of the snow drift with his horses. "Tain't horses, only mules". He did harness them up and with lots of shoveling and pushing, the jeep came back on the lane. We couldn't turn around, so we backed up the half mile. Charlie wouldn't trust my driving anymore, so he drove back to Buckhannon. I thought I would never get warm.

AN AUTOPSY WITHOUT PERMISSION

General practitioners sometimes perform major surgery in a hurry when an emergency arrives, and because of their training in a first-class medical school, they do very well.

Just before breakfast one morning in June, 1958, the hospital nurse called and said a maternity patient had had a seizure and would I come quickly. The patient was about eight months pregnant. She was in the hospital because she had a biopsy of a node on her neck the day before. After her biopsy, her doctor left for a meeting in San Francisco. He had assured me that she was fine and he anticipated her release from the hospital the next morning.

Sensing the urgency of the nurse's call, I hopped in my jeep immediately and started driving to the hospital which was nearby. Traffic was not busy, but I saw that the light was red. I looked both ways but didn't stop. As I went through the red light, I heard the police blow his siren. I proceeded to the hospital with the Chief of Police following. I arrived at the hospital within four minutes, but just in time to witness the patient have another seizure and die.

Thank God for good staff nurses and for Mrs. Smith's quick thinking that morning. "I'll help you with the C Section if you are ready." The instrument tray was opened and I made the first incision through the abdominal wall right to the uterus, and then through the uterus. Within thirty seconds, we delivered a seven pound girl who cried immediately. I was pleased, and somewhat surprised, to hear her cries. I had honestly thought we would have to resuscitate the newborn of a dead mother.

The phone rang in the room. The Chief of Police was on the line from downstairs where he had been waiting. I told him he could come up to talk with me. When he came up, he saw the bloody mess and saw me cleaning the newborn. I thought he was going to faint. I directed him to a chair. He

23

said that he wasn't going to give me a ticket this time, but asked me not to run a red light in the future.

When I looked at the baby, I was happy but scared to death. The baby was healthy, but I had performed a Cesarean without anyone's permission. Now I was faced with another dilemma. Should I do an autopsy on the mother? The report from the biopsied node in the mother's neck had indicated an infection, but I, the substitute doctor, had no idea why the seizure and why her sudden demise occurred.

I was more curious than scared, so I did a post mortem examination and took small specimens from the spleen, liver, stomach, kidneys, and adrenals, ovaries and the lymph nodes. I must have worked fast, because when the Catholic priest climbed the hospital stairs from the parsonage next door, he gave her last rites and baptized the baby.

I told the priest I would like to talk to him—I had no surgical permission to deliver the baby. He assured me he would take care of that little matter. Then I confessed that I had also done an autopsy without permission. I explained I really needed to know why the mother died and the baby needed to know also.

I called the baby's father and told him the good and the bad news—that he was the father of a healthy little girl, but that his wife had died.

The autopsy provided the diagnosis: Acute Lymphatic Leukemia which had spread to the brain.

The little girl, now grown up, graduated from college and is an accountant.

A JOYOUS, NOISY BIRTH

Both the young pregnant mother and her young husband were deaf. They were graduates of the West Virginia School for the Deaf in Romney, W.V. Their four-and-a-half-year-old son could hear normally and was bilingual. He spoke English at Kindergarten and to his grandmother who lived next door. He talked in sign language to his Mom and Dad.

The youngster taught me to sign for "It's a girl" and "It's a boy". He also wanted me to let him know if the baby cried out so he would know whether his sister or brother was going to be able to speak aloud to him.

He came to the delivery room with his mother because his dad was still at work. The smart little guy gave the hospital his mother's name, address, and even insurance information for all the paperwork.

I delivered a little girl that joyous day. Yes, she cried aloud which meant she would be able to speak. Her big brother was excited and happy for now he had a sister to talk with. He wouldn't even have to run over next door to speak to his grandmother.

This was one of the happiest births in which I ever participated. I still remember the sign for "It's a girl" and "Yes, she speaks English!" It was a happy foursome. It was a privilege on my part.

A SURPRISE CURE FOR ABDOMINAL PAIN

Early one morning I answered the telephone at home. A nurse from St. Joseph's Hospital was calling about a young female patient of mine who had come to the hospital with severe abdominal pain. A few minutes later, the nurse met me as I entered the hospital door. She said, "Maybe I'm wrong, but I took her to the maternity floor."

The patient's husband, holding their one-year-old child in his arms, said, "I sure hope you find out what's causing my wife's awful pain."

Not long after I arrived at the delivery room, I proved the nurse to be correct in her assessments. I delivered a healthy, full-term infant.

After the delivery, I went to speak to the patient's husband. He asked, "Did you find out what was causing my wife's pain?" When I told him he could go up to the maternity ward and see his new seven-and-a-half pound baby, his mouth dropped and he said, "Doc, you're funning me!"

During my hospital rounds the next day, the new mother said that she had planned to come in to see why she couldn't lose weight and what was causing "that churning around inside of me." To this day, I find it amazing that she had no idea that she was pregnant.

THE PAGE MANEUVER

Dr. Basil L. Page was buried in the West Virginia hills in his eighty-first year in 1981. The "Chief," as his friends and doctor colleagues called him, was a doctor's doctor. When the young doctors in Upshur County needed direction, they sought out Dr. Page. The following account illustrates this point and probably has assured Dr. Page as one of the greatest doctors in Upshur County in the 1900's.

The sick and troubled in Upshur County never had a better friend than the "Chief." Everyone recalls and remembers him as a surgeon, and he certainly was outstanding. Dr. Huffman said Dr. Page's eye was located at the tip of his right index finger, for he would locate a diseased appendix in a jiffy and he plated fractured bones so closely that the X-ray specialist looked twice to see the fracture. Among the young doctors in the late 1940's and early 1950's, the Chief was their teacher, especially in the field of obstetrics. Breech Births are particularly difficult to deliver, and in this particular type of delivery, the Chief helped us enormously.

A Breech birth, incidentally, is a baby coming with either its feet or breech first, and the head last. About four to five per cent of the Upshur County deliveries have been breeches. The difficulty comes because the head is the biggest part of the baby and complications occur when the baby's hands slip over the head instead of remaining by the baby's side. One hand over the head is an almost impossible delivery and two hands over compounds the disaster.

The Page Maneuver is used to correct this impossibility of hands over the head. The baby's hips and upper thighs are grasped with a moistened towel and the baby is turned 180 degrees back and forth until the lower hand either spontaneously returns to its side or can be easily placed at its side. If both hands are above, the 180-degree twist is done again and again until the second hand returns to its place.

27

This maneuver is simple and fast and does no harm to the mother or to the passenger, the little baby.

Breech births are not new, for recorded in Genesis, Chapter Thirty-eight is the tale of a woman with twins. The attendant doctor or midwife had a double problem for "the first put out his hand so she tied on a scarlet thread, the hand was pushed back and the first was a breech, and the second boy when he was born had a scarlet thread."

The attendant at that delivery 4000 years ago must have had anxious moments until the babies arrived. Sister Heriberta said she could always tell it was a breech delivery when the nurse, the anesthetist, and the doctor stopped talking. After the doctors and the nurses learned the Page Maneuver, it was all chit chat again.

The Page Maneuver applies to all God's creatures. Russell Westfall, a well-known local farmer, reported an interesting series of breech deliveries. The first occurred early one Saturday morning in October when a cow couldn't deliver her breech calf. Pulling on the legs exhausted the veterinarian and Russell so they used the block and tackle. The calf died and the cow was injured. Later on that same Saturday, Russell's son Lynn's prize cow was likewise with breech and couldn't be delivered. The veterinarian was on another call at the time so Russell Westfall, strawberry grower, corn husker, and producer of half runner beans turned obstetrician that afternoon. He had overheard me talking about the ease of the Page Maneuver, so he thought he would try it. He grabbed the calf's hind legs and twisted 180 degrees back and forth six or seven times and out popped a calf. Russell says the procedure works, and he only needed ordinary strength.

It spoils this story to tell you all that Dr. Page didn't discover this maneuver. He said he learned it some years before from Dr. Bill—but then, he was modest and nobody ever met Dr. Bill.

Dr. Page taught this method of breech delivery to the young doctors of St. Joseph's Hospital in 1949 and 1950 and they, in turn, taught it to others. In fact, only here in this little town in a small Appalachian state is this life-saving technique affectionately called the Page Maneuver.

THE DIAGNOSTICIAN

A NURSING STUDENT'S HEADACHES

She was our last office patient that December night in 1983. It was cold, wet, rainy and was near Christmas. My nurse commented that if a person was out on a night like this, then she must be sick. This young woman had been referred to this old doctor by her mother-in-law.

She looked sick, almost desperate. Desperate like she needed a stronger pain medication. "If you can't help me, then I don't want to live. My headache is ready to blow the top of my head off." She relayed this complaint with so much sincerity that I looked to see if the skull or her brown hair was coming loose.

She was young, only twenty-two, and was a hospital aide who was currently enrolled in a twelve-month course to advance herself to a Licensed Practical Nurse (an LPN).

The history of her headaches started fifteen to eighteen months before as a mild nuisance in the head and was easily controlled by an occasional aspirin. The nuisance became a misery and the misery became intense pain. Now the pain was "blowing her head off". Eighteen months ago, the nuisance occurred once or twice a month and now the pain came almost daily.

About twelve months ago, she had also started her LPN course. She loved it and many things she had learned as a hospital aide helped her get good grades. She had to study a lot; there was so much to learn and to memorize and to remember. She gave up her aide position. Then her husband lost his job. Next, the power company cut off the electric to their trailer, and now she and her husband and two young boys had moved in with her mother-in-law. Everything was going from bad to worse. She didn't feel like cooking, cleaning, or even playing with her two young sons. She would lie on the couch after supper watching her family, but lately, she realized that this was the time when she got her headaches.

31

After hearing her history, I began to think of all of the possibilities. She had already had her glasses checked. They were functioning very well. In migraine headaches, the patient usually smells or sees something odd about fifteen minutes or so before the headache. Also, with severe headache, the victim, like Lewis Carroll of Alice in Wonderland fame, usually sees some bizarre figure during the attack. He wrote, in that wonderful book, that Alice, at times, was so small that she couldn't see through the keyhole. Once, she was so small that she couldn't open her mouth because her jaw was on the floor. None of these characters were ever visualized in my young nurse patient with her severe headaches.

She had twice been to an excellent clinic in a nearby town. She had seen two third-year medical school residents in the Emergency Room. She had seen one of our younger local doctors. She had been told by everyone that she had tension headaches. The Lord knew, and I knew, that her schooling was tough. Final exams were ten days off. Money was non-existent for her family. Living with your family of four in the same trailer as your mother-in-law was ample cause for severe headaches.

Brain tumors cause headaches only in moderate to advanced states. My examination of her pupils, then her eye ground and optic nerve with the ophthalmoscope, showed no internal pressure within the skull. She was not dizzy when standing with her eyes closed. She could read fine print and could hear the watch tick. Her blood pressure and pulse were both normal. She was well aware of time, place, and person. She was smart. She would make a good LPN.

Her heart, lungs, abdomen, and limbs were all normal. She had good muscular coordination. But then, the night was cold and rainy and her mother-in-law had sent her to see the old doctor.

Doctors and nurses sometimes need a coffee break. It is time to think and remember. As I was drinking my coffee, I thought back through my years of experiences. In August, 1945 in the 580-bed Chicago hospital where I was an intern, I saw a thirty-two-year-old call girl with similar headaches to the ones described tonight. I recalled her saying that sometimes, when she was at work, those severe headaches would occur suddenly. I remember the attending physician and I palpating deep down in her abdomen, in the area of the kidneys, and one time we precipitated one of the devastating attacks of pain. Her pulse started to race from 72 to 120 and her blood pressure, which had been on high normal rate, now was astronomically high.

I asked the young nursing student if she had ever awakened at night with her heart pounding. She promptly stated, "Yes, and then I immediately get my headache!"

Finally, I could make a diagnosis of this nursing student—the same as the doctors had made in 1945. Both patients had tumors of the adrenal gland. Both tumors released adrenalin into the blood stream and immediately increased the heart rate and contracted the arteries and caused hypertension. It was as if they had received a shot of adrenalin. The adrenal glands are on top of the kidneys and secrete cortisone and adrenalin.

The young nursing student was hospitalized for two days; a twenty-four-hour urine specimen was positive for adrenalin-like compounds. Also, her blood pressure during three attacks was taken and compared with the basic pressure. All three readings were well over 200/130, with her normal being 138/86. The CAT scan was taken of her right adrenal and, sure enough, the tumor was found there just as her history had revealed. As she lay on her right side on the couch while she watched her young sons play on the trailer floor, the headache occurred.

We scheduled our patient for surgery right away to remove her tumor. The surgery is tricky because the tumor is about ½ x ½ x ¾" and while the surgeon isolates and ties off blood vessels, the blood pressure goes up and up and up. The anesthesiologist must, now and then, give a strong medication to lower the blood pressure. When the tumor is removed, the blood pressure falls rapidly to a very low level. Now, the patient needs medication to elevate the blood pressure.

The surgery was successful. The patient passed her State LPN Boards and soon enrolled in an RN course.

Coffee breaks are an institution among coffee-drinking doctors and nurses. So naturally, one morning when the mailman delivered the surgeon's report about this patient, I pondered his unusual inquiry over a cup of coffee. Since it was only this surgeon's second operation for a pheochromocytoma, he wondered whether I had another case.

33

As I knew, these are found in only one out of every 400,000 patients. Luckily for my nursing student that dreary night, I had beaten the odds by having seen two cases in my practice.

THE STARVING BABY

The call was thirty miles upstream to see a newborn baby whom I had delivered six weeks ago. The summer was 1955 and the baby was vomiting excessively.

The family lived in rural mountainous West Virginia, and the depression was still there for the uneducated and the unskilled. There were government commodities and a small welfare check, also free running water from a sweet water spring. There was an outhouse, plus bass and trout in the Buckhannon River. The garden was on a hillside, well-worked, but the yield was so-so.

The road was rock-based almost to the house, but I had to walk up the trail the last one hundred yards. The heat from the coal-wood range felt good that rainy afternoon, and the smell of old-fashioned blackberry jam in the making added temporarily to my spirits until I saw how sick the baby was.

The baby was a girl and had weighed 7 lbs. at birth. She had been healthy when she was born and her young mother, who loved her dearly, was breast-feeding her and trying to give her good care. Despite the loving care, the sick baby was off its 7 lbs. and down perhaps to about 5 ½ lbs. The vomiting was projectile and there were visible waves of movement in the stomach.

I made a quick, but educated, diagnosis. I believed the baby had pyloric stenosis. This was an unusual, almost unheard of, condition in my practice. The valve at the outlet of the stomach was congenitally thickened and wouldn't grow as the baby developed. The thickened circular muscle around this baby's pyloric valve was the cause of the vomiting. The baby was doomed unless operated upon immediately to relieve this obstruction.

My single experience was one case that I had seen in April, 1949. An Air Force Officer's son had a similar episode of vomiting, and I flew with him to a larger military hospital in southern Japan. The diagnosis was the same, a pyloric obstruction. The Air Force surgeons had invited me to assist in the operation. Here, I had seen my first Ramstedt operation to cut these circular muscles. Drip ether was used—about 5 or 6 drops per minute. The starved little boy in 1949 had barely awakened from surgery when he received formula. He was so starved he hung onto that nipple, and he took deep gulps of formula, one after another. There was no further vomiting; his constipation was gone and he gained 2 ozs. a day after surgery.

Now today, the sickness was the same, but money in this West Virginia home was nearly non-existent. The mountain mother and the sick little baby rode back in my jeep to St. Joseph's Hospital in Buckhannon.

I consulted with the two other general practitioners and our board-certified surgeon at St. Joseph's. None of the doctors had ever treated a baby with pyloric stenosis. We got out the surgery books and studied and studied. We really wanted to refer the baby to Richmond Medical School Hospital or to Cleveland Clinic Hospital, but the family didn't have enough money to get out of town.

Dr. Page, our board-certified surgeon, restudied the procedure and expressed his doubts, so I asked him if he would assist me. It was great to be young and be willing to take chances. Thank God, however, my eagerness to do the operation myself changed Dr. Page's mind. He said that he would do the surgery if I would help him tomorrow. The baby was now down to 5 lbs.

The next morning, Dr. Jake Huffman, our anesthesiologist of that day, dripped the 6 drops of ether per minute. I noticed he wasn't singing his patient to sleep this morning; in fact, he was all business. Dr. Page didn't whistle the one song he had memorized years ago. His mouth was too dry. The incision was one inch long over the outlet of the stomach and it was down through the right rectus muscle and through the peritoneum. The pylorus was found by Dr. Page's ever-seeing right index finger and was brought up into the field where all three of us and our two nurses took a good look. The circular muscles were cut and their elastic fibers retracted. The operation should have been over, but Dr. Page teased down to the mucosal lining of the pylorus, and a little hole appeared. No matter, the surgeon had done the same thing in 1949 and one stitch repaired the hole of the boy in

Japan. One stitch repaired the hole in central West Virginia that summer day in 1955. The peritoneum and the rectus muscle of the abdominal wall were sutured and the skin suturing was next. Now Dr. Huffman was singing another barber shop song. Dr. Page was whistling his one and only tune. When surgery is going well, everyone in the OR is relaxed.

Dr. Page dropped in the nursery after his next tonsillectomy operation to see the baby. Sister Heriberta and I were feeding the little girl. She was starved and she was gurgling her tune. It sounded to me even better than those sung by my dear operating colleagues.

"What are you two doing? You can't feed a baby so soon. She's not yet awake."

"Please, Dr. Page, you go back to your surgery and leave the feeding to us." He went away, whistling—all was well.

We at St. Joseph's did nine or ten identical cases in the next ten years. After Dr. Page retired, he said this was the most gratifying type of surgery he ever did for he saw the results instantly. He loved babies; no matter that he never got paid for over half of the pyloric stenosis operations he did.

A CHILD WITH A TRIGGER THUMB

It was the day after Thanksgiving and in the middle of deer hunting season. The patient had a trigger thumb. Not his trigger finger to be sure. He had awakened that morning and there it was, a thumb that was bent and could not be straightened. He was not in any pain. He was only two years old.

My knowledge of any trigger finger was limited to the one case of a railroad express employee at 12th Street Station in Chicago in 1946. He had traumatized his hand on the edge of boxes and caused a bruise of the tendon sheath of the right index finger. That Railroad express worker in 1946 had the swollen sheath cut and the blood and fluid were drained off.

But I had never heard of a trigger finger on a small child. I examined eighteen books at St. Joseph's Hospital and, in the nineteenth, I found that a trigger thumb on a baby is a congenital defect. The sheath doesn't grow, although the baby and the tendon grow. It is like putting a ring on a baby's finger; the baby and his finger grow but not the ring. The ring needs to be cut.

The little lad returned to his home in North Carolina where, at Duke Hospital, the surgeon made two one-quarter inch incisions over the sheath at the junction of the metacarpal bone of the hand where it meets the proximal bone in the thumb.

Will the two-year-old lad return to hunt in West Virginia? Yes, indeed. Some say he was just warming up his trigger finger.

HEART MURMUR VIA THE TELEPHONE

Dr. Basil Page, Buckhannon surgeon, was on the phone that late summer evening. His voice was troubled and urgent. "Listen to this heart murmur over the telephone." The murmur that I heard at my home that August night in 1954 was loud and crunchy. It was peculiar, to say the least. In fact, I had never heard a murmur without a stethoscope up to that minute. On some patients, I even have had to turn them on their left side and then I would strain to hear the auscultations.

My curiosity was aroused, so I grabbed my doctor's bag and my own stethoscope and headed for the patient's apartment. When I entered the home, Dr. Page said he had cured the murmur. Indeed, the twenty-two year-old male had a normal-sounding heart. I thought Dr. Page was up to his usual pranks, but then, the man's wife was crying. Dr. Page had the man sit forward in his chair, and that very loud crunchy murmur returned and could be heard across the room. Dr. Jake Huffman arrived, and there was a repeat performance. We couldn't even guess or give it a name.

Today, we would grade this as a Grade VI Murmur, i.e., one that can be heard without a stethoscope, as opposed to a Grade I, which can be barely heard with a good stethoscope in a noiseless environment. Dr. Page could make the murmur come by positioning the patient so that his heart would touch his rib on the midline, and the murmur would disappear with the patient on his back, or sitting down in a chair, or lying on his left side. It was a systolic in nature, that is, it occurred with the first of the two heart sounds.

The lad did not feel sick nor was he in pain. The loud murmur had suddenly, spontaneously occurred about half an hour before, and he called Dr. Page immediately.

Chest X-ray and EKG were normal. None of us yet knew the diagnosis.

Shortly after leaving the patient's home, I went to the hospital to help deliver a baby. During the night as I was waiting for the baby to arrive, I searched the medical books. At 4:30 a.m., I found, in an old Dr. Paul S. White cardiology book, a footnote that an air bubble in the media-stinum or a bubble in the space between the lungs could cause this murmur. The murmur was caused by the heart beating against this bubble of air in the space between the ribs. This is Hamman's Murmur, or sign.

For years, I made it a point to ask cardiac specialists about this murmur and few have ever heard of it. In fact, most are not aware of its existence. The patient recovered when the air bubble was absorbed. He had previously passed a Navy physical for admission to officers school but was rejected on the final examination.

THREE THINGS DOCTORS AND DETECTIVES MUST KNOW

It was a quiet, late summer night in the emergency room. Just then, a fifty-six-year-old chronic alcoholic entered through the door. He was not drinking now; he was just short of breath. In fact, he was hyperventilating about thirty-six times a minute. He was breathing deeply. His mouth was dry and he needed a swig of water before he could talk.

His story was that for the past three weeks he was short of breath and it was getting worse. No, he had not drunk any alcohol for three weeks. No, he didn't feel sick at all—he just wasn't breathing right. I tried to figure out why his breathing was so fast. People breathe rapidly when frightened to death, but only for short periods of time. Underwater swimmers who have no oxygen mask purposely hyperventilate so that when they dive down beneath the water, it is effortless not to breathe.

Early in World War II, our pilots pursued the Japanese zero fighter planes above 30,000 feet. But above 30,000 feet, even with their masks intact, they couldn't get enough oxygen and they started to hyperventilate. They reported to the flight surgeons that soon they were drooling at the mouth; their thumbs and toes were cramping; their vision was getting blurred. In addition, they lost control of their sphincters and it started to get cold up in the blue yonder.

Pre-med and chemistry majors in Freshman chemistry all recall a simple experiment: the student blows his expired air via a glass tube into the lime water. The clear lime water soon turns cloudy. Exhaled air contains carbon dioxide and water vapor. Start your car on a cold day and you realize how much water vapor you exhale. Combine water with carbon dioxide and carbonic acid is made.

When a pilot, a frightened person, or, in this case, a chronic alcoholic patient blows out an excessive amount of carbonic acid, then his blood is less acid or, as doctors say, he has a relative alkalosis. In fact, he must be in a strong acidotic condition. His body must be making an excess of acid.

Starvation and diabetes are common causes of acidosis but my patient was well fed. The test for sugar in the urine was negative. He was taking no medicines.

The key to a correct diagnosis was discovered by a microscopic examination of the patient's urine. The urine showed abnormal cells from the kidneys and its tubules. This signified that the kidneys were diseased. The kidney-function test revealed kidney failure and uremia. The uremia was serious, and the patient expired within three weeks.

His alcoholism was a bad habit, but was only a red herring in this case.

The old adage: Three things are necessary to be a good doctor or a good detective:

1. Acquire vast sums of knowledge
2. Have keen powers of observation
3. Arrive at some logical conclusion

In this case, the diagnosis was made in the emergency room with a urine test and one blood test for uremia. The doctor possessed the knowledge to ignore unrelated symptoms and draw a logical conclusion.

A FAMILY WITH HEADACHES

It was a Friday night and the nurse and I were with our last patient when the phone rang. It was a thirty-year-old mother asking for a prescription for her four-year-old daughter. The little girl had an infected throat and had used aspirin, but the aching and hurting persisted.

We invited the mother to bring the sick girl to the office. She balked at that idea, and I balked at filling a prescription for someone I hardly knew at all. The mother finally relented and soon brought her child in for an examination.

The little girl did have a mild pharyngitis and a little fever, but I could see no reason for the aching and the headache. She also had vomited several times. I was puzzled.

As the mother and daughter were leaving the examining room, I noticed the mother was unsteady on her feet. She, too, had a headache and was dizzy and she had vomited. The mother also said her seven-year-old girl, in the waiting room, had been dizzy, but she had missed no time from school.

I asked about her husband, but he had not felt sick. He was working a twelve-hour shift on an outdoor job. The other daughter, age eleven, had been well except for the last three nights when she complained of nausea and headaches.

With all of this information about the family, I suspected carbon monoxide gas poisoning, probably from a space heater. But, I discovered they had a gas furnace.

We examined the mother and seven-year-old girl. We arrived at the same diagnosis—carbon monoxide poisoning. I insisted that both of us—the mother and our office—would call the gas company in the morning. She also agreed that she would leave a window open in each bedroom that night.

On Saturday morning, my nurse called the gas company. They told her that they were already checking out the home.

On Monday, the mother called and told me that I had caused the seven-year-old to catch cold from the open windows. I was amused when I considered my possible life-saving recommendation, but I readily agreed to supply medicine free for her doctor-induced cold. Of course, I asked the question. I was extremely curious if my diagnosis had been correct.

The gas company found that the concrete top of the chimney had fallen in the flue as the result of ice and snow. Workmen removed the concrete pieces, and the headaches and dizziness were over. I felt good that my diagnosis had helped this family divert a disaster.

COTTON IS THE CLUE

One day in 1975 when I was covering the Hospital Emergency Room calls in my office, a young man was sent by the hospital to see me. He was about thirty years old and had a severe earache.

"Doc," he said, "I have been to two or three doctors and they treated me for an earache and I just don't get any better. Can you help me?"

I examined his ear and found both ears filled with wax, with some discharge that was foul smelling. I began to remove the wax and after some considerable effort and time, and some discomfort to the patient, I found some cotton in one ear.

I said to the patient, "How long have you had this cotton in your ear?" After an appropriate pause, "Well, Doc, seven years ago I went to Cleveland Clinic and had surgery on my ear and I never went back for a checkup."

After spending a half hour that day cleaning his ears, I sent him home with instructions to use two drops of mineral oil in each ear and to return in a week. Again, when he came back in a week, I spent a half hour cleaning wax out of his ears. Still having not completed the job, I sent him home again to continue using the mineral oil, two drops in each ear twice a day.

When he returned the third time, I was able to complete cleaning out both ears and see that the tympanic membranes in the ear canals basically were normal. However, in my efforts to clean his ears, there was some scratching in the canals and a tiny bit of swelling, so I asked him to return one more time.

A month later he came back and the ears were clean. The tympanic membranes and canals were clear and he appeared to be quite comfortable. When I asked him how he was doing, he said, "Doc, I can't stand the noise."

To this day, I have never heard from that patient again.

THE ARTHRITIC TRIGGER FINGER

She was fifty-six years old and a guard in the Goodyear Air Space Factory in Akron, Ohio. She had come home to visit her mother in central West Virginia. She was worried, so her mother sent her to her old doctor.

Her worry came from fearing that she would not be able to qualify in her upcoming guard test because of the arthritis in her trigger finger. Arthritis had nearly crippled her hands and modern medicines were good, but the trigger finger was not happy. It could hardly perform. She had taken the Akron specialist's medication, but it upset her stomach.

I knew of a practical, and usually successful, method to treat arthritis. Arthritis of the hand is best treated with melted paraffin—the paraffin on top of homemade jellies and jams. The paraffin is heated in a double boiler to prevent fires. A chunk of hard paraffin is dropped into the melted paraffin to test the temperature. If it melts, the paraffin is too hot. If it doesn't melt, it is about the right temperature for the hands. Heat therapy is an old, old treatment for arthritis, especially when the affected part can be placed in the same reheated paraffin baths again and again.

After three weeks of paraffin therapy at her mother's house, the guard returned to her Akron specialist for her test. She squeezed the bulb and the mercury shot to the top. Some even ended on the floor. The Ohio specialist was much pleased. "See, that medicine worked well," he told the factory guard. Her answer: "The treatment of that old West Virginia doctor saved my job, and it was cheap, too."

Today, in that specialist's office, an electrically controlled paraffin bath is part of his treatment.

X-RAY DIAGNOSIS

The patient was ambulatory and had probable renal disease. Enemas and laxatives were administered and the scout film of the abdomen, from the first ribs to the hips, had been taken. This scout film was done to be sure that there was no air over the kidneys or over the collecting tubules. Then, and only then, could I give the intravenous dye for the final diagnostic X-ray.

The X-ray specialist, Dr. Herman Seltz, from Elkins, picked up the film and instantly gave this diagnosis: "She is middle aged, has no teeth, and it is small game hunting season again. Oh, yes, she is cleaned out adequately. Go ahead and inject the dye."

The scout film had included only the first ribs downward to the hip bones. "How do you know that—how did you arrive at that instant diagnosis?"

"Easy, dear doctor, easy. The two breast shadows indicated her sex; lessening of the calcium in her vertebral back bones showed osteoporosis and thus middle age; and the multiple buckshot in her gastrointestinal tract meant she had no teeth. Nobody can eat rabbit or squirrel which has "shot" in its flesh unless they are toothless, and then they just swallow the game. Yes, it's hunting season in West Virginia."

Dr. Seltz was right with his instant diagnosis: the patient was a woman, she was middle-aged, and she had no teeth.

GOOD DETECTIVE DOCTORING

I hand-carried the x-ray film of my fifty-one-year-old patient to the x-ray reading room in the hospital where Dr. Robert Cunanan was at work interpreting the films. I was worried about this patient. I was puzzled as to the correct diagnosis. She had been my first patient after Thanksgiving, and I had examined her in the hospital Emergency Room. She said her eyes were bulging and she couldn't see clearly. She also said for the last seven days she couldn't breathe well and that her face and neck were swollen.

The first look showed the protruding eyes, the cyanosis of the skin on her face, neck, arms, and even her fingernails, and that her breathing was somewhat labored. A minute later she had to cough, then she breathed easier. Now that was paradoxical during this flu season. All the other patients had to stop coughing in order to get a breath.

Further examination revealed a normal size heart and normal heart sounds, the usual pulse of 72, and no congestion in her lungs. Blood pressure was normal in both arms. There was none of the cyanosis of her trunk, nor the lower feet and there was no swelling in the feet and ankles.

Over cups of coffee, two hospital nurses and I discussed this case and we reasoned that the veinous return from the head, shoulders and upper extremities were partially blocked, but the veinous return from the trunk and lower extremities was good.

I was worried and I was anxious to know the diagnosis, so I scarcely noticed the hospital x-ray technician take the picture, then process it.

Dr. Robert Cunanan placed the film in the viewing box and, about a minute later said: "your middle aged lady must have bulging eyes, swelling of her face and neck, shoulders, and finger tips. Also, she must have labored breathing and probably when she coughs she breathes better."

He had never seen the patient, and thus I was ready to call him Dr. Sherlock Holmes Cunanan. I had spent forty minutes in a history-taking physical examination followed by a reasoning session over a cup of coffee.

I asked him how he could make such an accurate diagnosis so quickly.

He answered, "Look here, Doctor, there is a small tumor in the right upper, outer lung field; it probably has spread to the midportion of that lung. That caused swelling of the lymph nodes and that, in turn, is causing an obstruction of the superior vena cava syndrome."

I asked Dr. Cunanan if this superior vena cava syndrome was common. I was speechless when he told me that, in all his years as a specialist he had looked for this syndrome, but this was his first case. He also told his staff and me that there are only two x-ray findings that are acute emergencies, and this was one of them.

My patient was admitted to a neighboring hospital immediately where x-ray therapy and chemical therapy could be started that day in order to shrink the obstructing mass that was blocking the superior vena cava.

The rest of the day I bragged about the excellent care that the X-ray specialist in our West Virginia hospital gave to my patient, and, of course, to all patients.

GETTING AN ERASER OUT OF HER NOSE

The ten-year old girl had lost the rubber eraser of her pencil up her right nostril. Her mother tried to get it out with a small pair of tweezers but had only succeeded in pushing the rubber tip further up her daughter's nose. The little girl wanted to go see her doctor, so the mother and child arrived at the office.

The rubber tip was far up the right nostril. I told the mother we could try a simple method to get it out. She blocked off her daughter's left nostril and blew as hard as she could into the girl's mouth. Out popped the rubber tip, much to the surprise of the little girl.

She looked at me and said with a smile, "Now, you are not going to charge me, are you? My mother did all the work!" "No," I said with amusement, "you owe your mother. Come back when I can help you."

When the blast of air goes through the patient's mouth with a sudden burst, the patient automatically closes her glottis and pharynx, and the blast of air comes out the other nostril. This method can only be tried once as children do not want to be experimented on but one time. There is no pain and no mess and it is over in a second.

After I helped my little patient get the eraser out of her nose, I started thinking about just what wonderful little machines our noses are.

The best furnace in Upshur County during this past winter of zero weather was your nose. This unit worked well; it took in zero degree air, moved it through your nasal tissue and converted it instantly to 98.6 degrees. God did this for you eighteen times per minute.

In addition, the humidity of the air was changed to 80% and impurities were removed. You also could smell Christmas odors at all degrees of temperature.

God also uses this same nasal tissue in summer when the temperature is over one hundred degrees. Hot air runs through the nose air conditioner to be reduced to 98.6 degrees. The beauty of this useful machine is that it costs nothing for us to operate if we take good care of it.

HE COULDN'T SEE THE SQUIRRELS

The seventy-four year old hunter from Webster County came to our office on Friday the 13th. His chief complaint was that he no longer could see the squirrels. He and his wife loved squirrel gravy. He had a few other complaints like shortness of breath from early heart failure and some crippling arthritis in his shoulder, but the reason he had come thirty-six miles to the office was his failing eye sight.

He was an outdoorsman and had worked in the woods most of his life. Inspection showed a mucous membrane growth partially covering over his pupils which was causing a cloud in his vision. Doctors and nurses call this a pterygium. A pterygium is a growth that is Mother Nature's way of putting on "sun glasses". This growth prevents strong sunlight from blocking out the visual portion of the eye.

All pterygium that I have seen since 1945 have been single and all grew from the nasal side of the face. My mountaineer patient had bilateral pterygia and the growth was from opposite sides or outer sides.

I seldom can guarantee a cure with certainty, but I sent my patient to our Buckhannon ophthalmologist, Dr. Jerry Black, who would instill a few drops of local anesthesia in his eyes and then remove this growth. My patient promised that, after the growth was removed, he would give me a squirrel tail for my grandson.

The February, 1989 issue of the <u>Journal of the American Medical Association</u> tells of an American doctor's encounter with a twenty-nine-year-old native woman in Saigon, Vietnam. She was the chief hostess in a bar, and she had developed bilateral pterygia. Her skin was brown and her pterygia were brown—dirty brown, she thought. Her eyes hurt and were red. She mistakenly thought that the smoke and the whiskey had caused the growth in her eyes. She gave up smoking and drinking, but to no avail. She thought her good looks were disappearing which meant that she would lose her job and be out on the street.

The American doctor assured her that he could help her. He wrote down the name of a Saigon ophthalmologist who would operate on her eyes. The woman seemed relieved about her eyes, but she was still troubled. The doctor and patient eyeballed one another again. He asked her what she saw, and she murmured something foreign to his ear. She then asked what the doctor saw in her eyes. His reply cured her depression and her acute anxiety: "I see a beautiful woman with no pterygia at all." She smiled, bowed low, and silently left his office. He never saw her again.

ANIMAL STORIES

ATTACK AT THE FARM POND

A doctor's practice in rural west Virginia is different from a practice in a city or a metropolitan area. It is more adventuresome. The unexpected is common. It is expected. The following exciting case comes to mind when I think of animals that attacked my patients.

The coal miner and his five-year-old son were enjoying the summer holiday by fishing in a farm pond. All of a sudden, the son screamed out in terror and the dad saw a small dog attacking his little boy. He dropped his pole and rushed to his son's side. He grabbed the animal by the neck and twisted off its head. Father and son hurried to the office that evening to see me.

The father's tale sounded like the dog had rabies, so I told the father that he should have brought the head in for microscopic study. The reply was "I did," so I sent my nurse to view the head and to see if we had a container suitable to put the specimen in.

My nurse came back looking like a ghost and vomiting. "It is the most hideous thing I have ever seen." Even I felt nauseous as I put the head in a glass jar to take to the Health Department the next morning. The dog was, in fact, a small red fox. As we always did to be safe with a potential rabies case, we started the first of fourteen rabies shots that night for both the father and the son. Laboratory tests later proved that the fox had rabies.

DOUBTING THE HEALTH DEPARTMENT

It was midmorning one August when a little four-year-old girl saw something moving in the tall grass. She was curious, and so she investigated the moving animal. It was a small bat. The bat bit her immediately. Her screams brought her mother. The mother grabbed the bat and placed it in a gallon jug, over which she threw a burlap potato sack. She found the jar lid, punctured it with air holes and headed for our Buckhannon office.

My Registered Nurse and I viewed the bat. We knew that healthy bats are not found on the ground at midmorning, but are sleeping in the trees for the day. We recalled that a month previously we had treated a miner's son for rabies when a fox bit him out at the fishing pond. The other incident had occurred about two miles away.

As was always my practice with rabies, I started the first of the fourteen painful rabies shots in the girl's abdominal wall that morning. We personally delivered the jar with the live bat to the Health Department Office for shipment to the laboratory. The laboratory froze, sliced, stained, and studied the brain tissue.

On the eighth day of treatment, the Health Department informed our office that the bat's brain did not show rabies. My nurse and I were surprised. We supposed that the animal pathologist was looking at a frozen section and not paraffin sliced tissue that had been stained. As an intern, I had seen frozen sections of breast tissue. Later, I had seen the same tissue prepared in paraffin, sliced, and stained with dyes. The frozen tissue was too difficult for me to read.

I mused over the telephone report from the Health Department—no rabies in the bat's brain? Eight days before, eight shots ago, I had been sure that the bat had to have rabies. There were six shots more—all to be given in the little girl's abdomen and all very painful. I was on the spot. My clinical judgment said "Yes, the bat had rabies." I was cautious. I gave my little patient the other shots. My worry was over.

About ten days later, an excited young woman from the State Health Department called. "Do you remember the little girl who had the bat bite?" We replied we couldn't forget her or the little boy who had been bitten by the fox. The voice quickly stated, "We had reported to you that the bat had no rabies, but in fact the paraffin test showed up the negri bodies. The test is positive!"

We startled her by telling her that we had already given the little girl all fourteen shots. We had not trusted that first report. With relief she asked, "You didn't believe our first report?" She must have turned to her boss, for we heard her say in a muffled voice: "Thank God, someone doesn't believe the Health Department!"

The Health Department representative warmed our hearts that day with her comment. We had made the right clinical decision. Our little girl would be all right.

THE DOCTOR'S DOG

I can't remember exactly when our family collie started to make country calls with me. I think perhaps it was after a local policeman asked me who I was talking to as I rode by one night in my little jeep. I was talking to myself out loud, partly to keep awake, but partly because it was lonely out there. Some trips were thirty miles to Helvetia and thirty miles back, often at thirty miles per hour over curvy roads. At any rate, the policeman's look was odd—a doctor talking to himself out loud! That's when Ralph started occupying the passenger's seat in the jeep.

Ralph was the son of a thoroughbred collie. Our family got him early in the fall. All winter our five children played hide and seek with Ralph. They hid his mouse, a glove, or a stocking. He loved to have a stick or a ball thrown and he loved to fetch it back. He was truly perpetual motion.

Ralph often accompanied me to my office. One afternoon, he went to the office with me where I was to see a sick baby. Lost in thought about the baby's sickness as I prepared to leave the house, I barely heard Lois' request to pick up her repaired shoes at the shoe store, which was right down the street from my office. I forgot, of course, to take the identification slip for the shoes—in fact, I left it on the kitchen table.

The baby was not too sick; I had worried needlessly. Yes, I remembered the shoes, but I couldn't find the identification slip. The shoemaker and his wife were patients, so I went to the store anyway. But once there, I realized that I didn't know the size, shape, color or what repairs had been done. There were some sixty or seventy pairs of shoes in the shop that day.

Empty-handed, I walked back to my jeep in my office parking lot where Ralph was waiting for me on the passenger's seat. He wagged his tail and wanted his nose rubbed. Ralph seemed to say he could help save me a trip home to get the identification slip. I had an idea.

Together, we returned promptly to the shoe repair shop and I told Ralph to "sic" the shoes. He started down the row and around past the customers and the owner. All were silent and all watched. Suddenly, Ralph's tail went around in circles as he picked up a brown pair of newly soled and heeled women's shoes and brought them to me.

The shoe repairman was speechless when I asked the price of the repairs for Lois' shoes, but fortunately his wife spoke up and took my money and placed the shoes in a poke.

"Did you get my shoes?" Lois asked on our return. "You forgot the slip. It is here on the table."

"Your shoes are in the bag here." I picked them up and handed them to her for her inspection. Yes, they were the right shoes. She knew I couldn't possibly have known which shoes to bring home. I grinned and asked her to give Ralph a hug and a slice of cheese for being my friend and companion and for having a good nose. Indeed, doctors need help from wives, children, nurses, and, at times, even from our dogs.

MY PROTECTOR

Man's best friend is his collie dog. The Almonds have had many collies in the past forty-eight years in Buckhannon. They have all been gentle, affectionate companions for the entire family. Most of our collies were named Brier or Brier Boy. Occasionally, we slipped in another name like Ralph, who was the son of a Brier.

One summer night, Brier of that day and I made a house call somewhere above Alexander. At 2:00 a.m. we slowed down our little jeep at the railroad crossing before climbing up the first hill. Early in 1950, it was unusual to ever meet a car after midnight once I left the city limits.

The tavern in the old Railway Express Office was closed, but I noticed five or six men loitering about. I heard one shout, "Let's get him!" I drove up that hill as fast as I could and much too fast on the straight stretch before the next hill, but their car caught up with me on the uphill and drove me off the road. One fellow ran around the jeep to the side door and opened it. In my fear and anger, I told Brier, "Get 'em"! Brier went crazy. He growled and bit the fellow across the wrist. He instinctively attacked that man to protect me. I shouted, "Mad dog!" The fellow dropped his idea of entering the jeep and screamed out loud to his companions, "Mad dog!"

I spun the wheel and up the hill we flew. I never knew if it was a hold-up for my little money, or if they were after drugs in my medical bag. This was the only time I was stopped or held up in my forty years of practice. Brier got a big hug and an extra slice of cheese when we got home that night.

COLLIE MEDICINE

At the office one morning, I shared a phone call with my staff because I did not know how to handle a problem that my patient was having.

A woman had called about her mother who lived in her home. The elderly mother, who was blind and bedfast, had called her daughter back to her room for the umpteenth time that morning, saying there was a boogy man under her bed. The daughter, for the umpteenth time, told her there was no boogy man. She even got down on her hands and knees and lifted back the covers. But the blind can't see and now the daughter, usually full of patience, was worn out and getting worried.

What kind of medicine could I give this elderly woman to ease her mind? Modern medicines are lifesaving, but even the psychotropics wouldn't work. Hypnotism? But then this doctor was not educated in that field.

When I entered the house, I was met by a big barking collie—but his wagging tail was a giveaway. He was friendly. It turned out, Shep was Grandmother's favorite—next to the grandchildren. Each day, he went back once or twice to see Grandmother.

Man's best friend turned out to be the doctor's best medicine, for he followed me back to Grandmother's room and, with a little urging and lifting, he put his heavy paws on Grandmother's abdomen. As the collie leaned against Grandmother, I commented on the weather, the crops, the grandchildren, their preacher, the latest T.V. news and a little about strawberries.

Grandmother was appreciative of the attention and the news, but then Shep was getting heavier as time passed. She stirred and changed her position, but then I deliberately told a story or two more. The sixty-pound collie became heavier and heavier for Grandmother the more I talked.

Finally, I asked the elderly woman if she liked her collie dog. When she had answered yes, I asked the dog to bark if he spotted a boogy man under the bed. Much to my relief, the big gentle collie stayed silent, and Grandmother was convinced that the boogy man was gone.

Suddenly, Grandmother told her daughter that she was hungry. She had been too worried to eat all day long. I bid the elderly woman good day and gave her big collie an affectionate rub before I headed back to my office.

THE WORST SNAKE BITE

Snake bites were not common in central West Virginia, but we Upshur County physicians collectively saw three or four cases each summer. Usually, snake bites are painful but not fatal when properly treated. However, our hospital staff always recalled one serious incident whenever the subject of snake bites came up for discussion at staff meetings.

It was one hour after dark and the young farmer's wife made her last call to the outside necessary house. A copperhead struck her on her instep and wouldn't let go with its fangs. Her husband came running when he heard her screams. He grabbed the snake by the neck and eased the fangs loose. (I suspect that the venom from that large snake must have been in a large quantity and must have been potent.)

I recall the phone call from the excited daughter. I still hear her mother crying out in pain. I gave directions for an ice bag and a tourniquet to be applied. The family brought the patient by car from Hacker Valley, some thirty-five miles away.

When the patient arrived at the hospital, her foot below the tourniquet was black. I injected the snake antivenin near the wound. We enlarged the bite and washed and re-washed. We applied the tourniquet up the leg in six-inch segments and gave more antivenin. We packed her foot in ice and gave her morphine for her pain. The patient was "a hurtin."

Eight or so times during the night the nurses loosened the tourniquet. I administered more antivenin. The patient's foot and ankle were as black as the starless night. By morning, the tourniquet was at the mid thigh. The foot, leg, and lower half of the thigh were black—oh so black. The bite was serious—the worst I had seen. Both the consulting doctor and I thought she would lose her leg and maybe her life. We gave her several blood transfusions. The wonders of the anesthesia were appreciated that night. For the next few days, we covered the snake bite of the lower extremity with ice. Fortunately, at that time, we could get all the ice we needed at the local ice plant.

Thankfully, appropriate medicine, good nursing, and lots of prayers brought about her recovery. And yes, that outside necessary house was properly set on fire as the husband had promised. He finished their inside bathroom before his wife was discharged from the hospital.

TREAT MY DOG FIRST

The telephone call was from a country store at Selbyville, thirty miles upstream from Buckhannon. The elderly patient lived another two miles up the stream from Selbyville, across two submarine bridges. She had been itching all over for three weeks. Now she had diarrhea, and she was out of her mind.

About ninety minutes after the call, I crossed the second submarine bridge, parked my little jeep, and headed up the country road. It was uphill, and I was soon out of breath. An old man standing in the intersection of the road asked me where I was going. I replied that I was the doctor. He seemed disappointed but he admitted that the patient was his wife. He said that he had expected one of the older doctors, not a young fellow. In fact, he told me I was too young to doctor his wife. I was now the disappointed one, having traveled thirty-two miles for no pay.

As I was contemplating my predicament, I noticed that the old man's coon dog had the same symptoms that had been described as those of the old man's wife. The dog was scratching himself, running around in circles, and had diarrhea.

I remembered back to my medical school days when I had seen Chicago folks who had scratching, diarrhea, and seemed to be out of their minds. Back then, we had been instructed by Dr. Tom Spies, a nutrition expert. He told us about the Four D's: dermatitis, diarrhea, dementia, and death. Over the phone, it had sounded like this patient had three of the D's so I had brought along niacin, vitamin pills, and even some big liver capsules. I had also brought along a bottle of intravenous niacin and thirteen other vitamins.

I stood there on the path thinking. If I couldn't treat the old man's wife, then would he let me treat his dog? Yes, he said, he is hardly a dog anymore. I offered the dog a handful of vitamin pills plus the liver capsules. The dog "woofed" them down.

Four days later, the Selbyville storekeeper called again. He told me I had cured the coon dog. I was invited up to treat the old lady, the man's wife. When I called on her, she had pellagra, the disease of the Four D's. I gave her the same medication I had given the old dog--vitamins, plus the liver capsules. I gave her a list of foods heavy in the B Complex vitamins. She, too, made a rapid recovery, and I treated that family for the next ten years or so.

THE RABID HORSE

Early in the 1950's, many farmers still used horses to plow their fields because West Virginia farms are hilly. The hills are too steep for tractors, and tractors cost several thousand dollars more than a team. Eventually, horses were replaced by a small tractor, but in the early part of my practice, horses were commonplace on farms. Seldom, however, did we ever see an injury caused by these normally gentle work horses.

One morning, we were paged at the hospital and the telephone report was that a farmer had been bitten by his rabid horse. At the hospital, I examined the farmer's bite. It was a nasty gash. The muscles about the shoulder were torn, and the deficit was four by eight inches. Dr. Page, our surgeon, worked hours restoring the farmer's injured muscles and tendons.

The hospital notified the Health Department, and they, in turn, employed the local vet to examine the horse's brain tissue. The farmer's diagnosis was correct. His horse did have rabies. We gave the farmer rabies, tetanus, penicillin, and gangrene shots and hospitalized him for several days. This is the only occasion in my practice that I knew of a rabid farm horse.

TEN MOST WANTED

Doctors and F.B.I. agents have one thing in common. They both have a list of their ten most wanted. The F.B.I. puts up a list with pictures in the U.S. Post Offices and West Virginia doctors post a warning story in the Hillbilly. In 1988, I became concerned about a small tick whose bite could prove deadly, so I wrote the following article for publication.

Tick bite fever of deer and white mice is a disease caused by the little tick with the orange belly. The tick is ixodes damnini, so I guess this must be a damnable disease to youngsters who get bitten by this tick. The tick itself is small, about as big as the "o" in "Ouch, I have just been bitten by a tick!"

If you have missed finding the tick, look for the rash in three to twenty-eight days. It is a chronic red rash with the raised area of the bite, and it grows to be six, twelve, or eighteen inches or more in size. It is like a brush fire; it spreads out or migrates outwardly and lasts for days. Doctors and nurses have a name for this chronic long-lasting red rash that migrates outwardly. Chronic Erythema Migrans is the official name, better known as Lyme Disease.

Can Lyme Disease be serious or just another chronic rash with pain? It can be both. This disease manifests itself with some of the following signs and symptoms: as a flu-like illness with fatigue, headache, fever, chills, sore throat, stiff neck, pain in the chest, leg or back; pain in muscles and joints with recurrent joint swelling; dizziness and sun sensitivity. It can cause meningitis and can be fatal. In pregnant women it can cause a miscarriage. Lyme Disease imitates juvenile arthritis in children and frequently is treated as arthritis but unsuccessfully.

Mice and deer carry the tick. Where a lot of deer are found so is this tick. It has not hit West Virginia too hard, but has been devastating in other states. First reported and identified in Lyme, Connecticut in 1975, Lyme Disease has infected a sizable per cent of the population of Connecticut and Massachusetts. Owners of private estates have taken down their "no hunting" signs and replaced them with "please hunt here with care". Lyme Disease out-numbers other tick illnesses—more than the better known Rocky Mountain Spotted Fever.

Chronic Erythema Migrans, or Lyme Disease, is on my personal "Ten Most Wanted" list. The tick, ixodes dammini, is very small, but the rash is large and can be readily diagnosed. The treatment with penicillin or tetracycline is effective. The real danger with this little tick is that most cases of Lyme Disease are in children.

THE ALBINO DEER

As I was driving to a house call at daylight one November morning in the early '50's, I heard a shot. I saw a white deer with a fine rack of horns fall beside the road. I then watched the pleased hunter quickly walk up to his deer. I knew the hunter, a local telephone repair man.

We were on a road just across the county line, upstream from Buckhannon. I knew that every hunter in the area had been after this unusual albino deer. I congratulated Chester for his kill, and I drove on to make my house call to the sick baby up the hollow.

On my return trip I saw my lucky hunter being arrested. Only buck deer with antlers were legal, and unfortunately, this freak white deer with horns was a female. The conservation officer, who had come upon the scene, was young and "gun ho" to enforce the law, especially when my hunter friend didn't want to be arrested.

Chester's blood pressure and weight were usually above normal, and I bet to myself that, at that moment, they were higher than ever. My prescription worked well that morning. I told Chester to accept being arrested but to demand a trial by jury with at least one hunter on the jury. The young officer said, "No jury would convict him so what is the use of charging him?" Tis true, I thought. You, young officer, are very intelligent and my friend Chester is lucky to be taking home his albino deer this morning.

MEDICAL EDUCATION

GUINEA PIG FOR THE WAR EFFORT

In early 1940 General McArthur reported that, after successfully fighting off zero planes, too many fighter pilots and their airplanes were lost by accidents on landing. These American pilots had flown without oxygen above the 16,000 foot mark and had used tank oxygen when they flew above 30,000 feet. To determine the effect of altitude on fighter pilots, an American physiologist supervised a study of medical students in a pressurized tank of oxygen.

At Northwestern Medical School, as a sophomore, I was one of the first guinea pigs in their simulated flight under pressure in a metal tank. The tank seated twelve of us medical students. We flew with oxygen from a tank in conditions that simulated 15,000 to 18,000 feet.

The oxygen was given to us at that altitude because of a common sense lesson we learn from nature. We were taught that when you hike at higher altitudes and start to run out of oxygen, you start to hyperventilate. But when you hyperventilate, you blow off additional carbon dioxide and water or H_2CO_3, i.e. carbonic acid. This leaves the blood in a relative alkaline condition. You start to notice you get spasms of the muscles, first in the fingers and hand. Your urine turns milky where calcium phosphate and calcium carbonate precipitate out. If you check your visual acuity, it would be less, i.e. your night vision is decreased. You get dizzy, you wet your pants, and you can easily stop breathing.

In addition to being given the oxygen during the study, we were fed a high vitamin, high protein diet at the local hospital. I gained five pounds in the three months of this experiment.

We studied the hour while flying in this metal chamber. We finally learned to swallow correctly and we able to descend from 60,000 feet to Chicago's altitude in four minutes.

We all were paid $1.00 a day for collecting all our urine daily for the three-month period. Toward the end of the experiment one night, the medical student next to me collapsed out of his seat, lost his oxygen mask, and landed on his chest face down. We all thought he had a heart attack. I was his neighbor to his left. I took two deep breaths, took off my oxygen mask and sat him up. Another student put the collapsed student's mask back on, and I staggered to my place. Still another classmate put my oxygen mask back on my face. I gasped for breath. Other students started the bells ringing to the outside graduate student and rang the bell throughout the seven story medical school. Dr. Andrew Ivy, physiologist and doctor and head of the department ran down from the fifth floor to his experiment.

We descended from 60,000 feet in four minutes. The collapsed medical student was breathing. He was rushed next door to the hospital. He had a spontaneous pneumothorax, which is a spontaneous collapse of his lung, cause unknown. I felt fully recovered, but Dr. Ivy wanted me to go the hospital. I told him I had to study for his examination the next day. He said I would pass the exam if I would go over to the hospital. I was checked out and was found to be healthy. I studied a couple of hours and passed the test on my own the next day.

General McArthur passed a law that all pilots flying with oxygen would have to fly over the flying field for fifteen minutes any time they had flown over 15,000 feet with an oxygen mask. All pilots were fed a high vitamin, high protein diet. The accident rate on landing was greatly reduced.

The medical student with the collapsed lung recovered and saw service with the Coast Guard after graduation.

MEDICAL SCHOOL

In the late summer of 1945, I was a senior at Northwestern Medical School. Like all medical students in the past forty or fifty years, it was my turn to deliver babies for the Chicago Medical Center. All deliveries, if they were normal, would be delivered in homes throughout the city. The first week medical students were the assistants; the second week, they delivered. Backing up us students were residents and attending physicians if anything went wrong. More serious cases were referred to Cook County Hospital where 7,200 babies were delivered by their interns, residents, and attending physicians each year.

The Chicago Medical Center was located in the near southwest part of the city on Halstead Street. There were clean rooms where we students slept or talked with one another. There were clinic weekdays for the pregnant women to visit and to be assessed by the student, resident, or by the attending physician.

These homes where deliveries were made usually had running water but not always hot. A thick layer of newspapers that had been saved by the mother was used as sheets for the delivery.

All of us carried the satchel instrument bags, emblazoned with the insignia of a pregnant mother and a newborn baby. Every policeman, bus driver, trolley conductor in the city would stop his vehicle if he saw a young doctor carrying that famous city-wide insignia.

One day, a call came in about 3:00 p.m. that a newborn's umbilical cord was leaking a drop of blood. I walked the two and a half blocks to the baby's address and was welcomed. As I entered the small apartment, I didn't see the baby. The mother said he was in the next room. In the next room, I found no crib, no bed, and, in fact, no baby. I returned and asked the mother where the baby was. She said he was in that room in a cage. I found him asleep in the cage and tied a new knot in his umbilical cord and the oozing stopped. When I asked the mother why the baby was sleeping in a cage, she told me that another newborn baby in their apartment building had his thumb eaten the week before by a rat, so she put her baby boy in a cage for his own protection.

A night or two later we took the street car north on Halstead for about a mile and found the address to be located in an old store, now boarded up with a thick old white curtain. We entered the building to find six gypsy men sitting on wooden stools, carving wood with long knives. On the opposite side of the room seven men were doing likewise. My senior partner and I asked where the mother was. One gypsy pointed with his knife toward an inner room. We two medical students checked the pregnant lady, now in active labor. I was the junior member of the team that week, so I left my partner with the mother and went outside to find a telephone. This was the standard operating procedure, to call back to the Medical Center and report the progress. There was a light in a bar, half a block south, so I walked down to it. It looked like a tough, grimy joint. As I entered, the bartender recognized the maternity center insignia and said, "The phone is over there, Doctor." I called the Center, reported the progress, and went outside. A large Chicago City policeman was walking his late night beat. "What are you doing in this neighborhood at this hour, Doctor?" I told him my partner and I were up the block at that lighted store delivering a baby. "My God, a man was stabbed to death there ten days ago." He called for help and within ten minutes six other officers were there. We entered the store again with the six policemen and their drawn guns. As soon as we heard the baby cry and made sure he was all right, we rapidly cleaned up the site of our recent delivery and left that address to eleven gypsy men and the mother and her newborn son.

One night later, this same classmate, who was a Chicago native, and I went down to about 30th Street in a rough section of town. About 2:00 a.m., we found the correct street but could only locate the street numbers above and below the address of the resident in labor. Then we realized the patient lived down the alley between the other two numbers in an old carriage house. Up the stairs we met our patient, a very large woman who was very much pregnant. It was cold that morning so I asked my partner to light the kerosene heater.

He did, and it burst into flames. The patient kicked the door open and then she kicked the blazing stove down the stairs. It rolled down the alley and under our car. We hastened down and began pushing the old car. The pregnant woman in labor was pushing as hard as we were. The car didn't move at first, then it started rolling. We kicked the stove out into the center of the street and went back into the house. That mother delivered ten minutes later. It was by far the most spontaneous, uncomplicated delivery that either of us ever saw up to that time.

INTERNSHIP

Internship at St. Luke's Hospital in Chicago in 1946 and 1947 was the most interesting and meaningful eighteen months of my life. The hospital had 580 beds with an older building for the rich and the newer nineteen-story building for the poor and rich to share alike. It had a School of Nursing and students from University of Illinois and Northwestern University worked hard there to become educated healers.

In May, 1946, I was assigned to the emergency room 7:00 p.m. to 7:00 a.m. every other night. I also worked the Clinic from 8:00 a.m. to 5:00 p.m. week days. Here the poor could receive good medical help.

One morning, I was working the Pediatric Clinic, and I saw a chubby, eleven-year-old girl. She had been born at St. Luke's and had all her shots and exams here at the clinic. This morning, she was getting her yearly physical which was paid for by the Health Department. I examined her and found that she had no breath sounds in her right lung. It was also dull to percussion. She was not complaining and was not sick. She was referred to X-ray for a routine chest X-ray. The chief at that department called me in to talk about this patient. The X-ray seemed to be a puzzle. It looked like muscle and hair. He wished that I would order up an overexposed film, which I did. The film showed the girl had a tooth, or a teratoma, in her lung.

A teratoma is fetal tissue usually found in the ovary or testes. It is fetal tissue that started to grow with hair, muscle, teeth, bone, etc., but never develops because of a poor blood supply. It is known as "a little monster". The chest surgeon removed the tissue from the right lung and the girl was fine. This is not a cancerous tissue; it is fetal tissue growing where it should not be.

This so-called little monster is rare, but not unusual. Its presence in this young girl gave me the opportunity to give a unique presentation at the Clinical Pathological Conference that next Friday.

One summer night, a police ambulance brought a gangster from the Loop in Chicago to St. Luke's Hospital. Our hospital was the nearest hospital to the Loop, or downtown Chicago. The patient had received a bullet through his intestinal tract. We sent him from the Emergency Room to the surgical floor to get patched up right away.

One hour later, the night nurse and I were chatting with the hospital policeman. The hospital policeman's beat was the hospital, the church, the student nursing quarters, and a large printing office.

The doors leading to the ambulance office were thrown open and two men burst in and covered us with their guns. My heart jumped. I was sure these were some thugs after the man we had admitted an hour ago. I was much relieved when the beat officer said, "It is OK, Sergeant." The police had been notified that some gangsters were, indeed, going to return and try to finish off their botched job of the man they had shot. My mouth had gone dry and the nurse and I were speechless. I dreamed that night of the police and Chicago gangsters.

Another night in August, 1946, the LeSalle Hotel in the Loop caught fire in the bar. It had highly polished woodwork and couches and stools that burned with a hot flame. The fire spread to the nearby elevators and up the fifteen stories quickly. Few people were burned, but many became asphyxiated from the fumes.

Our first notification was two ambulances with four patients. The ambulance drivers said there would be over fifty more people coming immediately.

Fortunately for me as the Intern on call that night, I had the best nurse in the hospital. She was the assistant chief nurse in the nursing school. She had worked in the frontier nursing service in Kentucky. She was tops. She efficiently told me to "Press the red button for all thirty Interns, the six Residents, and the Junior Attending Staff." "Call the chief of the hospital, Dr. Brown, and tell him I said to get his butt down here." I called. Dr. Brown said we could handle it alone, but I told him my nurse said to "get his butt down here." He came.

The nurse listed all admissions, their names, ages if known or guessed at, their diagnoses, home addresses if possible, and room and floor numbers, the attending doctor assigned to that patient, all the while helping me and other doctors bandage, give shots, and dress burns. She even managed to talk to every new patient. She was worth her weight in gold. I loved my wife, but that night I loved my assistant. We, she and I, admitted fifty-five patients, including five dead to the morgue.

She supplied the list with the above information to the Chicago newspapers two hours after our first patient, assigned a student nurse to each patient, and directed the hospital nursing staff to help with the care for the wounded and burned patients that night. The hospital chaplain said we, but he really meant she, "handled this emergency like we did that work every night."

The last patient admitted from the Hotel LeSalle was a sailor from Great Lakes whose dad had come down from Wisconsin for a visit. His dad was one of our dead. The sailor was brain dead. He was asphyxiated with smoke. I checked him at 1:00 a.m. on the fifth floor. He was covered by the Medical Service but no one had seen him yet. I did his history, did the physical, and posted the diagnosis. I gave nasal oxygen that night, hoping he might recover, but at 7:00 a.m. he was still brain dead. He couldn't talk, eat, or control his bladder. The chief doctor of University of Illinois neurology department was hired by the Navy to care for him and at 1:00 p.m. the next day, I recited my findings to this doctor. He agreed with my diagnosis and thanked me for the sailor's care. The doctor notified the Navy and transferred the sailor to Great Lakes Naval Hospital, just north of Chicago. The sailor was brain damaged for life.

ST. JOSEPH'S HOSPITAL

ST. JOSEPH'S HOSPITAL'S EARLY DAYS

When I first came to Buckhannon, I was immediately impressed with the quality of St. Joseph's Hospital. The hospital building, itself, was old and not modernized but it was extremely well run by the Catholic Sisters. In those early years, the Sisters took care of the garden, milked the cow, and fed the chickens in addition to taking care of patients, performing laboratory tests, giving anesthetics, assisting with deliveries, and teaching young girls to be RN's. St. Joseph's had a School of Nursing back then and did a fine job of training and teaching.

In the 1950's, those of us on staff performed multiple tasks to make sure that a small hospital like ours offered comprehensive care. Sister Matilda, the Administrator, was the lab and X-Ray technician as well as EKG technician. She was also a nurse. In fact, Sister Matilda was one in a thousand nurses. She could and did it all well and did it all for years. The hospital had no Pathologist in charge and no X-Ray specialist to read the X-Ray films. Dr. Page read them all once a month. I had a short course in EKG reading at Columbia Medical School, so I read all the EKG's from 1950 until 1970 when the hospital accepted internists to the staff. We then shared the interpretations of the Q,R,S, and T waves.

St. Joseph's Hospital had one of only four elevators in Upshur County in 1950. It was extremely busy taking us from the ground floor to the third floor nursery.

The Emergency Room at St. Joseph's was started in 1956 by Sister Agnestine and me. It was a small room on the first floor that rented for $6.00 a day as a private room. The steam pipes overhead afforded themselves as poles for I.V. fluids. The average use was about one patient per day, but within a year, the census was up to ten patients per day. About the third month of use, the Emergency Room opened up the eyes of everyone in town when doctors helped save the life of a sixteen-year old shooting victim.

TRYING TO SAVE A TEENAGE SHOOTING VICTIM

The busiest day, and the most exhausting, I ever had started at 9:30 p.m. February 18, 1957. It had already been a trying day with home calls, cases of flu, and office visits. Now it was really continuing with a bang.

Dorothy was a sixteen-year-old who was sitting in a local restaurant with some friends when a thirty-year-old jealous suitor shot her three times through the abdomen, once through the right lung and liver, and once through her hand. The already long day thus became longer that 9:30 p.m. when the local funeral home ambulance and a patrolman appeared at St. Joseph's Hospital.

The bullet holes from the .25 caliber automatic pistol were evident, as was the fact that the sixteen-year-old girl was in shock. My training in a big, Chicago hospital as an emergency doctor was called up.

We started plasma in two separate veins, and drew blood for typing and cross matching and for blood counts. X-rays showed three bullets still in the abdomen.

It seemed like the whole town was there at the Emergency Room that night to help out. We obtained some twenty pints of blood and used seventeen of them.

We called in the surgical team of Drs. Page and Huffman, as well as the scrub nurse for the next day's operating schedule. One of the Sisters acted as the circulating nurse that night.

The worst wound was the bullet through the right lung that traveled forward and tore a hole in the liver before continuing through the stomach. The belly was filled with blood and most of it was coming from the torn liver. Dr. Page tied off the spurting vessel. Then he packed the liver with 36" of foam and 36" of gauze.

Now we began the critical and, at times, consuming, task of examining nine feet of large bowel and eighteen feet of small bowel. All in all, the surgical team found seventeen bullet holes in the stomach, duodenum, small bowel, and colon. All were sutured with catgut.

Dorothy remained in the hospital for the next five months. She had a rubber tube drain placed in her right lung. Her daily temperature was from 104° and 106° for about a month. Dr. Page and Charleston specialist Dr. James Walker operated and resected the 9th and 19th right ribs on March 30, 1957 so that the right lung could drain better. Another part of a rib was resected on May 10th, and the pus cavity in the lung was again drained.

Dorothy returned home on July 3rd with a tube still in her lung . She received daily dressings at my office for the next six weeks. She developed an abscess in the area of where the liver had been shattered by the bullet and was readmitted for an operation on August 24th.

Dorothy was poor and Welfare paid but only a token of the amount for the extensive care she got from the Hospital and three doctors.

She reentered school in the fall, but developed pneumonia March 30, 1958 and died after being hospitalized for thirty days. Shortly after she died in April, 1958, Dr. Page and I performed an autopsy at 3:00 a.m. with the following results: pneumonia in both lungs, chronic kidney damage, subacute infection in the heart muscles, and severe congestion in the liver.

This tragic case shows one man at his worst and a hospital and its nursing and medical staff at its best. Adversity generally brings out the best in men and women— this time the best was at St. Joseph's Hospital in Buckhannon.

ASK, SEEK AND KNOCK ON THE DOOR

He was twenty, cyanotic and gasping for his breath when the ambulance crew knocked on the ER door one night when I was working my shift. A blood embolus from a leg had thrown him into shock. At 2:00 a.m. his skin was black, and he was fading fast. He did not respond to nasal oxygen I administered while he was sitting in an oxygen tent; his blood pressure was zero/zero and heart rate 300 plus.

The night nurse didn't quite correctly hear the young patient's plea: "God help me! God help me!" Her answer, "We'll help you," puzzled me, but then she promptly said, "Dear God, help all three of us."

The I.V. digitalis slowed the heart rate, other medication raised his blood pressure, and by morning he was half alive. By mid-morning, he was out of danger.

I later thought to myself: Ask and it will be given, seek and you will find, and knock and the door will be opened.

WATCHES AND GLOVES

Vi, the head nurse at the Pap clinic that day, said, "Doctor, why do you pull the glove over your wrist watch? Why not remove it entirely?"

"I'm a watch tester, Vi," I jokingly answered. The nurse shrugged her shoulders and elevated her eyebrows. "What is the story? You are the only doctor I know who does not remove his watch in the office or in the clinic and in minor surgery."

Sometime early in the 1950's, Lois and I went to the Alumni dinner at Wesleyan College in Buckhannon. Across the banquet table was the professor of chemistry and his wife from Glenville State College.

Professor Richard Brook was wearing one of the most beautiful watches I had ever seen, and I told him so. He took off the wrist watch and scooted it across the table. "It is yours." I refused, and in fact, I was embarrassed and felt like a beggar. Professor Brook sensed my embarrassment so he explained. "Would you like to be a watch tester and have a watch like this? My sister runs the program out of the Connecticut office. Timex is now testing their sound-proof, water-proof, scratch-proof watches with a new powerful battery that runs the watch for two years. Also, they are testing a watch that has no battery and nothing to wind." I thought that the watch he described sounded great. I could just move my wrist eleventy-eleven times during the day and the watch kept a ticking.

About ten days later, I received a similar watch—just as beautiful. A return box contained a note stating that in nine or so months, I would be notified, and I was to return the watch for another.

Never in my days in college, or in medical school, or in my fifteen months internship without pay, could I afford any watch like the one on my wrist that day. I used a watch 98% of the time only to use the second hand to count a pulse. I seldom paid much time as to the hour. Here, now, I was checking the hour and minutes and second hand many times that eventful day.

The next day, I needed to slip on a rubber glove to perform a vaginal and a rectal exam. I found myself taking off the watch and putting it in my pocket. But, I am a watch tester of a sound, water, vibrator proof watch. Why take off the watch? Yes, I am a watch tester.

Perhaps seven to ten times each day, I pulled a sterile glove over that watch and thought nothing of it. Nine months came and I sent the watch back to Connecticut. I got a new watch for my left wrist.

About a week after I had returned the first watch, I received a phone call from Miss Brook, the professor's sister, who asked me in a perplexed voice what I did for a living. I told her that I was a doctor in rural West Virginia. "What else?" she asked. I told her that I was also taught a course at West Virginia Wesleyan College.

After her call, I wondered why she was puzzled about my profession and how it related to my testing of the wrist watch. Finally, on a call that night to Helvetia, I realized I was probably the only watch-tester who pulled a rubber glove over his watch.

I called the next day and asked Miss Brook if they had found white powder inside their watch. She replied that the laboratory had, but they didn't know what it was. I explained to her that our office cleaned, washed, and sterilized our gloves and used Johnson's Baby Powder to slide them over the hand. The white foreign material in the watch was baby powder.

A day or two after, Miss Brook called again and wondered if her company could send me two wrist watches to wear. I laughed and told her I did all examinations with my left hand.

For the next nine years or so, I received a new watch to be tested about every nine months and I returned the old one.

Little did I and the chief nurse of the Pap Clinic realize on that day in 1957 that by 1985, all the hospital nurses, lab technicians and many doctors would be wearing many pairs of gloves all day long. The reason, of course, is the AIDS epidemic. So in a small way, Timex Watch Company and I were testing their watches for the future.

HONORING OTHER DOCTORS

MARCH 30TH - DOCTOR'S DAY

March 30th is Doctor's Day! This is the day, observed annually, on which we honor members of the medical profession with some act of kindness, gift or tribute to the untiring devotion doctors demonstrate as they minister to our health and welfare.

The red carnation is the symbol of Doctor's Day and was adopted as the official flower in 1929. The analogy of the carnation is so closely woven in medical science, it is only fitting that this flower was chosen to honor doctors. Crown coronation denotes honorary distinction. The color denotes masculinity, love, charity, sacrifice, bravery and courage.

The date, March 30th, was not chosen at random, but was selected to commemorate one of the greatest discoveries in medical history. It was on March 30, 1842, that twenty-six-year-old Dr. Crawford W. Long, a Georgia physician, first used ether as an anesthetic agent in a surgical operation, thereby providing mankind with the blessedness of freedom from pain and suffering during surgery. Thus did this quiet, young country doctor, by this stroke of genius, prove to himself and the world that "my profession is to me as ministry from God". Dr. Long died in 1878 at the age of sixty-two with forty of his years devoted to the practice of medicine. A statue of Dr. Long is located in the hall leading to the Senate wing of the U.S. Capitol in Washington.

Eudora Brown Almond (no relation to me) is the originator of the idea of Doctor's Day. She was born in the small Georgia village of Fort Lamar, and from early childhood, was greatly impressed with the selfless devotion of the medical profession's humanitarian service.

In 1920 she married Dr. Charles B. Almond and lived in Winder, Georgia. As she walked through the years beside her husband, sharing the dedication of his life to the practice of medicine, Mrs. Almond became convinced that medicine is the greatest profession on earth. When suggesting that physicians be honored, she originally had in mind only the Winder and Barrow counties in Georgia. After the resolution to pay tribute to the doctors was adopted in the two counties, the resolution was presented to the Georgia State Medical Auxiliary and it was adopted.

It was then most appropriate that they chose March 30th as the day for Doctor's Day to honor and pay tribute to the great son of the state of Georgia, Dr. Crawford W. Long, the discoverer of anesthesia.

The Resolution to honor doctors on March 30th was presented to the Southern Medical Association at their annual meeting held in St. Louis. It was adopted in 1935 and since then, has become an integral part and synonymous with the Southern Medical Association. Now we have Doctor's Day observances in all parts of the country and in foreign countries as well.

THE BUTTONHOLE SURGEON

One hundred years ago on the 2nd of March, 1889, John B. Murphy, a red-headed, fiery surgeon in Chicago did the first appendectomy before the appendix ruptured. Yes, it was customary in that day only to operate after the appendix ruptured.

One hundred years later, almost to the day, a Buckhannon surgeon and a Buckhannon urologist made history again by removing an appendix that had not ruptured.

Dr. Frank Hartman II and Dr. Peter Auriemma had been referred a 59-year-old man who was difficult to diagnose. It was a puzzle. This man had a misery in his lower right abdomen for several days after lifting a heavy object. He had no loss of appetite, no fever, but he had some blood cells in his urine. On a barium enema X-ray study, he had an irregular mass in his lower right colon. The X-ray specialist thought that he might have a tumor. The barium X-ray outlined the junction of the small and large bowel as well as the appendix.

The classical symptoms and signs of appendicitis start with misery about the naval, loss of appetite, and then the pain migrates to and settles in the right lower abdominal quadrant. These were the observations made by Dr. John B. Murphy on his patient one hundred years ago.

These clues were not the reason for the operation on Dr. Hartman's patient in 1989. His patient had a hard mass in the right lower abdomen and this mass was resected and the small ¾-inch bowel was sutured end to end to the 1¾-inch large bowel.

Truth is stranger than fiction. Dr. John B. Murphy not only taught surgeons to operate before the appendix ruptured, but he taught surgeons the world over how to suture intestines end to end in 1892.

John B. Murphy operated on his patient with drip ether. Dr. Hartman had his nurse/anesthesiologist put the patient to sleep with a pentothal sleeping injection, and he used an

95

intravenous dose of a muscle relaxant and a narcotic. Dr. Hartman's operating room copilots were a competent set of nurses, an RN and an LPN.

All anastomoses of the big and little intestines, up to 1892, were sutured side to side. Then, in 1893, according to Loyal Davis, Dr. Murphy's biographer and Nancy Reagan's father, John Murphy invented the Murphy button that slipped inside the two open ends of the intestine and allowed the intestinal membrane to be placed in apposition to each other. The button looks like a sleigh bell and it comes in two pieces; the outer shell that fits tightly to the inner tube.

Healing takes place without sutures over the button. The two halves of the button are further held together with catgut that lasts about eight to ten days before dissolving. In that eight to ten days, the cut ends of the intestine heal together. There are small buttons for small bowels and for children, and there are larger buttons for the big bowel and for adults.

All surgeons of the day learned this surgical procedure, which could be done in 15 to 20 minutes, thus saving 60 to 90 minutes of operating time. All the surgeons, including Dr. Murphy, soon realized they could do direct end-to-end anastomies without buttons.

When the pathologist at St. Joseph's in Buckhannon studied the surgical specimen of this 59-year-old patient, this mass was found to be an acute appendicitis invaginated into the larger bowel.

Dr. Robert Chamberlain, the attending physician, reported his patient did well and he was most happy to find that he had no tumor but only an acute appendicitis. His patient had feared having a ruptured appendix because his brother had died the year before of an appendicitis abscess and peritonitis.

Every doctor is indebted to his profession. Dr. Hartman is thus thankful to Dr. Murphy for teaching him, and all doctors, to operate on a non-ruptured inflamed appendix and how to suture intestines end to end.

Pause on St. Patrick's Day and think of John B. Murphy. Pause, too, on Doctors Day, the 30th of March, and think of some kindness, some sacrifice, some emergency medical service that your doctor provided for you or your family.

THANKS FOR DOCTOR JAKE

(In November of 1988, Rev. Frank Shaffer, our local United Methodist pastor, wrote an article for the Buckhannon Record/Delta. I wanted to include this article in my book because Rev. Shaffer did such a nice job of paying tribute to my highly-respected colleague and my friend, Dr. Jake Huffman.)

Just the other day, "Doc" Almond and I were talking about Dr. Jake Huffman who is presently a patient at St. Joseph's Hospital after suffering a stroke. Dr. Almond asked me "Do you know why Jake Huffman is such a great man?" I answered, "Well, I suppose it's because of all the patients he's attended through the years, all the babies he's delivered, all his involvement in our community and with the West Virginia University Hospital."

"Sure, it's all that and one more thing," Doc said. "Jake's a great man because of the city's water tank above this hospital." Then he went on to tell me this story.

In 1960, when the new hospital was being constructed, the developers ran into what seemed an insurmountable obstacle. The Fire Marshall suddenly declared that the 25,000 gallon stand-by water tank, perfectly adequate for the old Barlow House Hospital, would not have the capacity to serve the new one.

Everyone who had had anything to do with the building of the hospital—the Catholic nuns who were the hospital administrators, medical staff, board of directors, architects, and ordinary citizens of Upshur County who had already raised $200,000—were in a state of shock.

The West Virginia Board of Health had already approved the hospital plans and made a matching grant. That grant, however, was strictly a one-time thing. In fact, no grant recipient could apply for or secure a second such grant for any unexpected expense whatever.

The City of Buckhannon had only one water tank for the entire community, and water pressure was very poor on hospital hill, as well as on Lincoln and Riley Heights, Corhart, and in the whole west end of town. The Fire Chief had given a standing order that any time a fire broke out on hospital hill, the first truck was sent immediately to the scene. But the second truck was to be dispatched to the fire hydrant at Pinnell and Franklin Streets to increase water pressure with its pumps.

Many interested groups met repeatedly to discuss this new crisis regarding the Fire Marshall's notice that the old tank was inadequate. Even the city council met, but no helpful decision was forthcoming. There simply was no additional money because resources had been strained to the limit already.

At this dark hour, Jake Huffman was called upon to be the man "who stands in the gap". He didn't volunteer for the assignment which might more properly have been the responsibility of the architects. The hospital administrator, and others, asked Jake in a prayerful way to make the trip to Charleston to seek the apparently impossible—to get more money from the State Board of Health.

Jake needed someone to keep him company on the way to Charleston, so his friend and longtime colleague, Dr. Almond, went along for the ride. All the way down along curvy highways that one had to drive before Interstate 79, Jake talked of many things, chatting about this and that, but not once did he talk about his coming meeting or what he would say. Dr. Almond remembers that while Jake talked, his own mouth was dry with anxiety and anticipation. That night he could hardly eat his supper and sleep didn't come till late that night in the old Daniel Boone Hotel.

The following morning, the two good doctors shared breakfast with a woman who was a member of the Board of Health, but she gave no encouragement at all. At the formal hearing later that day, reactions were mixed, but the Board listened to Jake and his silent partner with courtesy. Jake argued, "We just can't plan a hospital construction under these inconsistent rulings. The Fire Marshall has changed his requirements long after his original ruling had been announced and accepted."

Jake noticed that one of the doctors on the Board, a physician from Bluefield, was nodding his head in agreement, but the chair of the Board, who had a great deal of influence, was firmly against any reversal of the ruling.

Nevertheless, Jake was elated and talkative as the two doctors made their return trip up the Elk River that evening, though his silent partner was even more silent.

The result: the State Board of Health reversed itself and awarded St. Joseph's Hospital an additional $62,500. The City of Buckhannon agreed to secure the same amount, and the land was donated by the Edmiston and Iden families. Dr. Almond says, "Some call it the Hospital Water Tank, but that's a misnomer. It should respectfully be called Huffman's Water Tank." Jake earned that respect because he convinced the Board of Health to reverse itself, which allowed construction of the new hospital in Buckhannon to move forward. He even went on to be the city and county health officer for twenty-four years.

TRIBUTES TO DOCTOR CHAMBERLAIN

Dr. Robert Luikart Chamberlain retired from delivering babies in Upshur County and at St. Joseph's Hospital in December of 1988. Dr. Bob, as he is known at the hospital and loved by his maternity patients, was delivered by Dr. Luikart in Marshall County. Appropriately, Luikart Forceps is the type that Dr. Bob preferred to use in difficult deliveries. In another twist of names, it must be noted that the first forceps ever made in 1600 were called Chamberler Forceps, named for their inventor, Dr. Chamberler. No one can argue that Dr. Robert Luikart Chamberlain, whose first love is obstetrics, has a name that is well-suited.

Dr. Chamberlain was feted December 18, 1987 by a large group of seventy people representing the medical staff, administration, family, nurses, aids, and other hospital personnel.

Dr. Chamberlain recalled that one time Sister Heriberta told him after a delivery of a boy that he need not circumcise the baby, that St. Peter had already done it. Sure enough, that infant boy didn't need a circumcision.

A hospital R.N. recalled a delivery that needs to be retold. Dr. Chamberlain saw a gravida II, a lady with one child, who came to the emergency room complaining of "appendicitis" pain for twenty-four hours. She said the pain rolled around her entire abdomen. Shortly after admission, Dr. Chamberlain delivered a baby and the appendicitis was cured. The husband could hardly believe Dr. Chamberlain's congratulations.

Dr. Jake Huffman welcomed Dr. Chamberlain to Buckhannon in 1949, and he was most generous in helping the young doctor build up an obstetrical practice. He delivered about 365 per year in that period which were way too many for one doctor.

Even after Dr. Bob retired from his obstetrics practice in 1988, he remained active in his office and hospital and college practice for several more years.

On April 15, 1989 at the annual medical meeting of the American Academy of Family Physicians of West Virginia, Dr. Robert Chamberlain received the prestigious award of "Mr. Doc".

This is a very special award given by his peers to a West Virginia physician for being an outstanding doctor and for involvement in community affairs.

Dr. Chamberlain had been a family physician in Buckhannon on the staff of St. Joseph's Hospital since August 1949. He had been the West Virginia Wesleyan student clinic physician and sports physician since 1949.

In his busy practice, he delivered over 2,400 babies, including twenty-seven sets of twins.

He was a member of the Upshur County Board of Education for over thirty years, a member of the First United Methodist Church choir for forty years, a participant in local plays and musicals from college days, and an avid golfer when he found the time.

Dr. Chamberlain graduated from West Virginia Wesleyan in 1942 and attended West Virginia University Medical School for two years, graduating from Richmond Medical School in 1945. He served two years in the U.S. Navy from 1945-1947. He is married and the father of five children.

If a Mountaineer calls a physician "Doctor," he is showing respect. If he calls him "Mr. Doc," he is showing respect and love—a deserving tribute to Dr. Robert Chamberlain.

DOCTOR CUNNINGHAM

SIXTY-FIVE YEARS OF DOCTORING

During my forty years of practice in Buckhannon, I came to love the West Virginia hills. I traveled throughout three or four counties making house calls and getting acquainted with back roads and strong, good-hearted people. One of my favorite spots in all of West Virginia is the little town of Pickens. This charming town, nestled high in the mountains about thirty-five miles from our home in Buckhannon, is the snow capital of West Virginia. It has the distinction of having more snow recorded at its weather station than any other of the state's seventy-seven stations.

Not only did I enjoy Pickens for its charming scenery, I came to greatly admire the people who lived there. One of the citizens I admired the most, and had the privilege to call my friend, was Dr. James L. Cunningham.

Dr. Cunningham, a physician in Pickens for sixty-five years, lived to be 102 ½ years old. At the time of his death in 1965, he was the oldest doctor in the United States. I met him early on in my practice and was his doctor the last four years of his life. As a young doctor, I marveled at his life's experiences and his extensive knowledge of medicine.

James Cunningham, born in 1863, became a school teacher at the age of eighteen and taught for seven years in Hacker Valley. In 1888, he determined to go to medical school. In 1891, he graduated from Baltimore University Medical College. He returned to West Virginia after graduation, and in 1894 he married Mary Roberts and built a home in Pickens.

During most of his sixty-five-year practice, Dr. Cunningham was the sole physician in his town. He also served as doctor for the families in Helvetia and Hacker Valley. He sutured their lacerations, dispensed their medications, treated their polio, pneumonia, flu, and typhoid, and even became their dentist when necessary.

Dr. Cunningham had all of the problems of any doctor in practice with the worries of his patients. Each patient's

105

ailment was a diagnostic case, sometimes being solved at the moment but other times requiring studying and reading. This was not easy without a hospital, X-rays, telephones, modern roads, or a laboratory. But until his eyesight began to fail at about 101, Dr. Cunningham tried to keep up with his medical study and reading. His only request for Father's Day in 1963, the year he turned one hundred, was a new medical text book.

Aside from doctoring, Dr. Cunningham found time to take on many other civic duties as school board representative, weather observer, agricultural advisor, census taker, railroad surgeon, poll worker, and friend to all residents, especially children. He planted more corn than his family could use each year so that the older children of Pickens could have a "secret" corn roast each summer. He convinced farmers in his area to use lime on their land. He believed everyone should receive an education and was able to get new schools built for the residents of his community.

Dr. Cunningham traveled the area on foot, by horse, by rail scooter and train, and he had one of the first Model T's in the territory. He usually had three horses so he could rotate them when one got tired. He wore out, or at least outlived, fourteen horses that he rode over the 3,900-foot Turkey Bone Mountain trail to the little villages of Newlon, Czar, and Jerico. His daughter, Mabel, remembered one particularly cold, snowy night when her father returned from a house call on his horse. He was frozen to his horse and needed her assistance to get out of the saddle.

Remarkably, Dr. Cunningham delivered 3,600 babies at home and never lost a mother. Statistics are dull figures to be sure, but if the average home delivery is over eight hours, Dr. Cunningham must have worked ten years on an eight-hour day, seven days a week just to accommodate old Doctor Stork. They made doctors stronger in Dr. Cunningham's day; he delivered his last baby when he was ninety-four years old.

Dr. Cunningham provided extraordinary care for his patients as was shown by the low two percent mortality rate of his 1300 typhoid patients and his excellent care of patients in the 1930 flu epidemic. Dr. Cunningham believed that any success he may have had during his long and fruitful years as a physician at Pickens was due to the help of his many friends, his dear wife Mary, his daughter Mabel, and to the Almighty.

DR. CUNNINGHAM TREATS A LEPER

In 1906, Dr. Cunningham gained notoriety in the state and in the nation when he took care of George Rashid, a construction worker who had contracted Hensen's Disease, better known as leprosy. Mr. Rashid, a Syrian immigrant, was working for the Baltimore and Ohio Railroad Company in West Virginia at the time the leprosy was discovered. Without medication available to cure leprosy in 1906, the disease caused panic among all railroad workers. The only treatment for lepers was to place them in remote isolation.

After the Syrian government insisted, President Teddy Roosevelt ordered the B&O Railroad to get medical care for Mr. Rashid. The Railroad company transported the patient in a railroad boxcar to the "end of the line" at Pickens, West Virginia. The only supplies the B&O sent were a revolver and a tent.

Dr. Cunningham, never exhibiting fear for his own life, provided humane treatment for his patient. Little was known about leprosy treatment in 1906. In fact, Dr. Cunningham was the only doctor in West Virginia who ever had a leper as a patient. Even today, with drugs such as promin, rifampicim, and clofazimine available for treating leprosy, the disease still carries the Biblical stigma of the unclean. Hopefully, with the leprosy bacilli now being grown in the foot pads of Nude mice and in the abdomens of armadillos, a vaccine will be developed in the near future. Despite the fear and stigma attached to leprosy, Dr. Cunningham displayed remarkable compassion and professionalism in his treatment of Mr. Rashid. Throughout his lifetime, Dr. Cunningham retained an interest in the treatment of leprosy. Even when he was over one hundred years old, he would frequently ask me, "What's new in leprosy?"

AN IMPORTANT BIG TOE

Before Dr. Cunningham sat a fourteen year old farm boy from up the mountain south of Pickens. He had been scything on his dad's farm in order to cut the filth. The scythe had hit a snag and the boy nearly cut off his big toe. It was 1906, long before antibiotics, so Dr. Cunningham scrubbed the foot and toe very well. He approximated the bone and severed the fascia with absorbable gut. He sutured the muscle, approximated the nerve and artery and sutured the skin with silk. All instruments and sutures had been previously autoclaved in his steam autoclave. He applied a wooden splint to keep the bone edges in apposition. The bone and the toe healed in six weeks and the boy had no infection.

Frank Fahrion, the fourteen-year-old boy who had his severed toe reattached in Dr. Cunningham's office, graduated from Pickens High School a few years later and attended West Virginia Wesleyan College in 1911. Two years later, he matriculated to the Naval Academy in Annapolis. He passed the physical exam for admission to the Academy and graduated four years later. That Pickens farm boy became Admiral Fahrion. As Admiral, he was in charge of all destroyers in the Atlantic in World War II and of all vessels about the Island of Bikini in the Pacific when America detonated the first atomic bomb.

Frank Fahrion was fortunate to grow up in Pickens, a small community located thirty-six miles up stream from Buckhannon. This young man would never have passed his physical to the Naval Academy, and never become an Admiral, unless he had all his toes in good-working order. Doctor Cunningham was a miracle worker that day when he repaired the fourteen-year-old's severely cut big toe.

Incidentally, Frank Fahrion's grandfather, who had settled in Pickens after the Civil War as a surveyor, was the cannoneer who shot the first cannon ball fired in the first land battle of the Civil War. That cannon ball was fired at

Philippi, West Virginia. The cannon shattered the leg of a Confederate soldier named Hanger. After his leg was shattered, Hanger went back to his dad's farm in Virginia and moped about for a year or two. One day, he cut out a peg leg from a piece of apple wood. He made such a good leg that other soldiers with amputations wanted one like his. Today, Hanger Instrument Company is one of the world's largest companies specializing in making prosthetics.

OPERATING UNDER WATER

In 1908, Dr. Cunningham demonstrated his great medical skills when he was required to be the orthopedic surgeon, the nurse, and the anesthetist. One cool morning in May, a tram railroad transporting logs from Hacker Valley to Pickens on the main line of the B&O Railroad crashed through a wooden bridge over the Buckhannon River. The tram pinned the fireman under the water. A fellow railroadman lifted the fireman's chin above the water and another worker ran to wake up Dr. Cunningham. Dr. Cunningham listened to the details of the accident and then grabbed his sterilized instruments and his chloroform bottle. He rode his horse down to the site of the accident.

Dr. Cunningham looked over the situation and knew that an immediate operation was necessary to save the fireman's life. The doctor poured the chloroform; he threaded the needles; he applied his blood pressure cuff to shut off the blood supply to the injured leg to control the bleeding. As the anesthetist, he anesthetized his patient with the chloroform drip. Every ten minutes or so, he added ten more drops. He then took the role of surgeon and walked into about eighteen inches of water to proceed with the operation. He tied off the femoral artery and vein, then cut and used his gigli saw to amputate the femur. Finally, he pulled the patient out of the water, up on the sheet, and sewed the muscles and fascia together.

Chloroform is an excellent anesthesia, but the doctor must be careful. If a patient gets too much chloroform and stops breathing, his heart has already stopped. It is a tricky anesthesia, but that is what Dr. Cunningham used successfully up there in Pickens, even in many home deliveries. He never lost a mother.

While Dr. Cunningham was a patient in 1961 at St. Joseph's Hospital, he told us younger doctors his story of the railroad fireman. "Did the man live?" I asked. "Why, yes! I saw him around Pickens for the next ten years. Right after his amputation healed, I went to my apple orchard and made him a peg leg." "Why apple wood, Doctor?" I asked. "Apple doesn't expand when it gets wet, and doesn't contract when it dries out," he told me. Dr. Cunningham always amazed me with his common sense and practical knowledge of how to solve medical problems.

DOCTOR CUNNINGHAM'S 100TH BIRTHDAY

When Dr. Cunningham turned one hundred years old in September of 1963, he was the oldest living physician in the state of West Virginia and one of its most famous citizens. He received birthday greetings from President John Kennedy, U.S. Senator Jennings Randolph, U.S. Representative Harley Staggers, American Medical Association President Dr. Annis, West Virginia Governor W.W. Barron, and Naval Admiral Frank Fahrion. His life's history was featured in the American Medical News.

The Pickens' farm women and his patient friends gathered at his hillside office-home, which also served as a library and pharmacy, to honor their beloved doctor. Also helping him celebrate were the first patient he ever delivered in 1894 and the last patient he ever delivered only six years before when he was ninety-four years old.

I was there on that September day to help Dr. Cunningham celebrate, too, but I had personally honored him several months before his official birth date during a snowstorm. In 1963, Governor Barron decreed that every West Virginian who turned one hundred years of age that year would receive one hundred roses on Valentine's Day. You see, the state of West Virginia also turned one hundred years old in 1963, and the Governor knew that the personal delivery of these roses would be a good public relations event for the state.

What the Governor hadn't counted on was delivery to the snow capital of West Virginia in the middle of February. Over two hundred inches of snow fell during the winter of 1962-63. On Valentine's Day, the State Police from Elkins couldn't get through the snow on the four mountains between Mill Creek and Helvetia-Pickens. Coincidentally on February 14th, I got a telephone call from the Pickens telephone operator to come up there to see a sick baby. She told me that I could make it through the snow in my jeep, and she told me, too, about the one hundred roses that had been promised but could not be delivered.

Shirley, the daughter of a cousin of Lois, who was also a second-year nursing student at West Virginia University, was visiting our home that week. I asked her if she would like to make a house call to Pickens. She enthusiastically agreed. We traveled through the snow to see the sick baby in Pickens. Afterward, we visited old Dr. Cunningham at his house on the hill. I had brought one rose, all I could afford, and I asked Shirley to pin it on Dr. Cunningham's lapel. He asked us about the storm and thanked us for coming to see him. My little jeep felt 10° warmer on the trip home that night. I was proud to help the Governor honor such a great physician on that snowy Valentine's Day.

A POETIC TRIBUTE TO DR. CUNNINGHAM

Written in 1972 by his neighbor Reba M. Bee

It was in the year of 1881,
That Doctor settled near our town,
He came here with his parents,
There were very few people around.

He first became a teacher
And taught the Golden Rule,
He was also a census taker
Then went to medical school.

For years he traveled on a horse,
Went out in snow, sleet and rain,
He used a speeder and a motor car
And sometimes he rode the train.

In later years he bought a car
In which he made his calls,
Our country roads were very rough,
He didn't seem to mind at all.

He delivered 3,600 babies
And he helped save many lives,
He also cared for the leper
That is buried at the wye.

He was a dedicated Doctor
He was ready at a call,
He took care of many people
Sometimes his pay was small.

He worked well past ninety
And still looked very young,
He lived to be one hundred
Yes one hundred and one.

In 1894 he married Mary Roberts
And had two daughters so dear,
Their names were Mabel and Ethel
They lived here on the hill.

They were always very kind
And helped until the end,
They always thought of others
They were very grateful friends.

They will always be remembered
For their deeds and acts of cheer.
We will always think of them
And feel that they are near.